ella

sets sail

For Mo, who always supported my sense of adventure – C.D.

And for Miranda and Remi.

ISBN 978-0-545-25841-8

Arthur A. Levine Books hardcover edition published by
Arthur A. Levine Books, an imprint of Scholastic Inc., June 2008.

12 11 10 9 8 7 6 5 4 3 2 1 10 11 12 13 14 15/0

Printed in the U.S.A. 40

First paperback printing, May 2010
Book design by Steven D'Amico and David Saylor
The text was set in 20-point Aged.

by carmela & steven d'amico

SCHOLASTIC INC.
New York Toronto London Auckland
Sydney Mexico City New Delhi Hong Kong

GLACES

The Elephant Islands Carnival had come to Little Village.

Ella was meeting her friends there.

"Have fun," her mother called.

"I will!" Ella waved. She'd looked forward to the carnival all summer.

But halfway there, a strong gust of wind knocked her hat off her head.

Ella sighed. "I can't believe it. What could be more unlucky?"

By the time she found her friends, the rain had almost stopped. "What should we do first?" Ella asked.

"I must win one of those parrots!" said Belinda, stamping her foot.

“It’s no use,” Frankie warned. “The game is fixed.”

“It never hurts to try,” said Ella.

“That’s right!” Belinda agreed. “Let me borrow a coin, Ella. Please? Just one?”

“What happened to your money?” asked Ella.

“I already spent it,” Belinda said.

Reluctantly, Ella handed Belinda a coin.

"I know!" shouted Belinda. "You don't want your coin to go to waste, right? So let me borrow your lucky hat, too."

"Well...I'm not sure."

"Pretty please?" Belinda begged.

"Oh, all right," Ella said.

While Belinda waited in line, Frankie and Ella and Tiki played around in the House of Mirrors.

"I'm so big!" Ella gasped.

"Look how long my legs are!" Tiki giggled.

Outside, the Parrot Man began shutting down his booth for the day.

"Sorry, folks! The parrots aren't so fond of stormy weather," he explained.

Belinda decided to cheer herself up by spending the coin Ella had lent her...

…on one last Ferris wheel ride.
"Where's Belinda?" Tiki asked.
"Up there!" Frankie pointed.
"And there goes my hat!" Ella cried.

"I have to get it!" she exclaimed, and took off running through the crowd.

Ella looked all around for her hat.

CLOSED

Finally, she found it.

Where is Mr. Pelican? she wondered. *If he knew how important this was, I know he'd let me borrow a boat.*

Ella had to row far and fast to catch up with her hat.

"I've got it!" she said.

The rain was falling harder. The waves were growing taller. Ella tried to row back to shore, but the boat drifted farther and farther away.

I'll use my lucky hat as a sail, she thought. *It's never failed me before!*

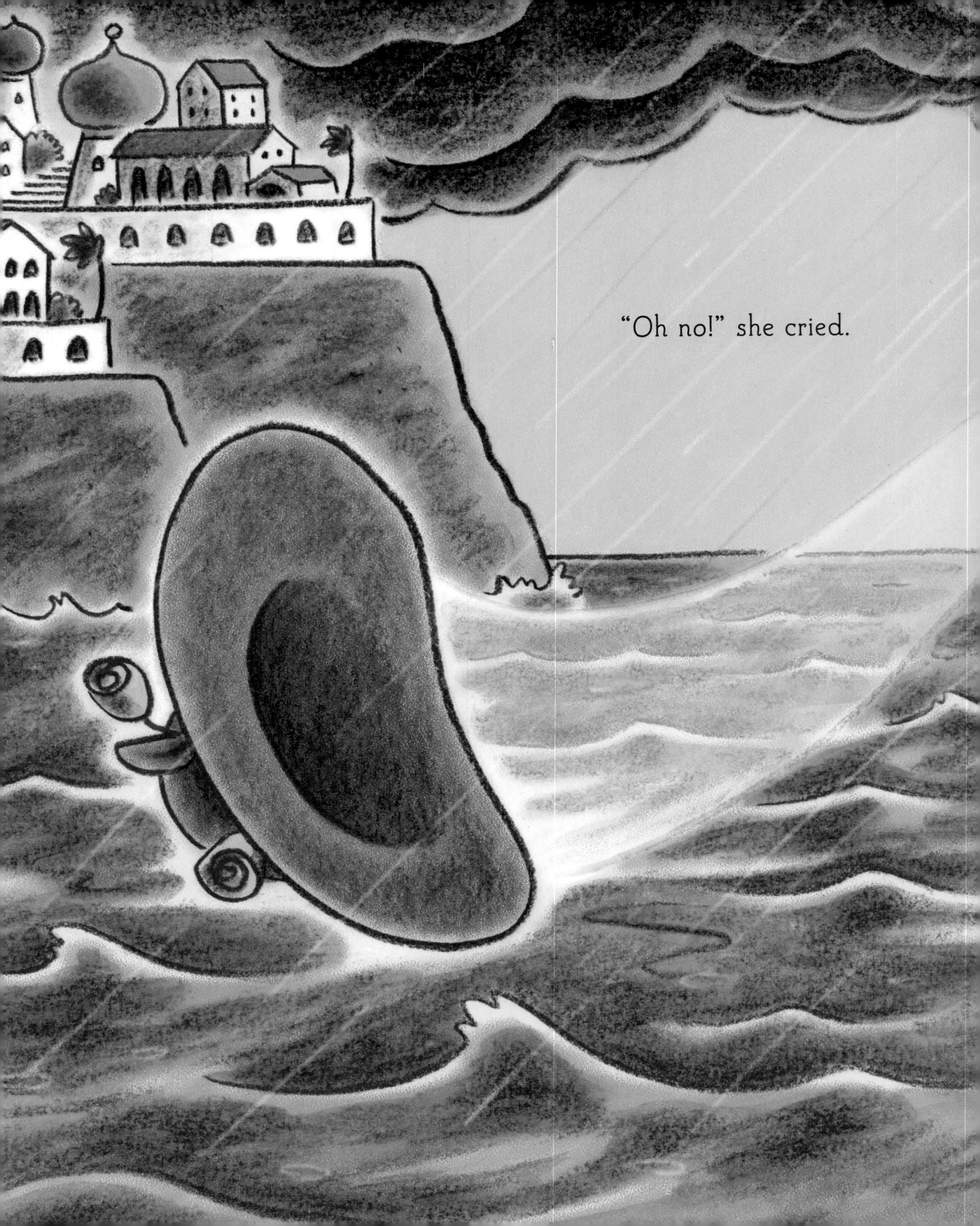

“Oh no!” she cried.

Had she ever had a day in her life that was more unlucky than this one?

At last, the boat washed ashore on an
island she'd never visited before.

Ella wandered into town.

"Would you like to come in out of this terrible weather?" a kind voice called.

"Thank you," Ella said, and burst into tears.
Then she told them about her very bad luck,
and how her hat had blown away after all.

"Well, you're safe now," Mrs. Spindle smiled, "and just in time for lunch."

The children asked lots of questions about Little Village and her mother's bakery.

"You've never had pineapple pie?" Ella asked.

"Never," the children said.

Soon, Mr. Spindle arrived.

He said to his wife, "I have something for you. A fancy thing it is, too! Got caught up in our fishing net during the final haul."

Ella was thrilled to see her hat, but she didn't want to ruin Mr. Spindle's gift.

The storm had passed, so she had to hurry home.

"Good-bye," Ella said. "You've made me feel so welcome."

"Hold on there," Mrs. Spindle said. "Aren't you forgetting something? What's the chance of another red hat turning up in a fisherman's net?"

"Oh, thank you!" Ella said.

"Good-bye!" shouted the children. "Come back soon!"
"I will!" Ella waved as she started home.

Ella arrived to find Mr. Pelican busy fixing a boat.

"You must have bananas between your ears, taking a boat out during a storm like that," he called.

"I'm sorry," Ella said.

"Well," Mr. Pelican grumbled. "You're just lucky nothing happened to my boat."

"Ella, where have you been? We've been looking all over for you," said her mother.

"Sorry about your hat," said Belinda. "It was an accident, honest."

"I'm glad you're okay," said Frankie.

"Yeah," Tiki agreed.

Walking back to the bakery, Ella told them everything that had happened.

bakery
bakery

"Goodness, Ella!" her mother said. "That was some adventure! But promise me you'll never take a boat out in stormy weather again."

"Don't worry," she said. "I promise. I won't."

Ella asked, "Could we bake a pineapple pie?"

"Certainly," said her mother. "May I ask what for?"

"It's a surprise," Ella answered.

The next morning Ella headed back to the docks with a freshly baked pineapple pie to share with her new friends.

"You really gave me a scare yesterday," Mr. Pelican scolded. "You're lucky I don't tell your mother. You're lucky you're alive. You're lucky—"

"You're absolutely right," Ella said, smiling...

"I *am* lucky."

David
Smit
Drawing +
Sculpting

OUR SEVENTY SIXTH YEAR
J. E. SAWYER & CO., Inc.
STEEL · HARDWARE · MILL SUPPLIES
Power Tools & Drives, Belting, Copper & Brass, Paints & Varnishes
Modern Plumbing Fixtures · Water Systems & Heaters
Efficient Home Heating · Boilers · Oil Burners · Heating Supplies
FREE ONE HOUR PARKING AREA
DIAL 2-0953
64-78 GLEN ST.,
GLENS FALLS, N.Y.
SEPTEMBER · 1959
9th MONTH
30 DAYS
SUN MON TUE WED THU FRI SAT
1 2 3 4 5
6 7 8 9 10 11 12
13 14 15 16 17 18 19
20 21 22 23 24 25 26
27 28 29 30
JOHN W. TAILLON

TARGET

8-8-57

David Smith: Drawing + Sculpting

Steven Nash
Candida Smith

Nasher Sculpture Center

David Smith: Drawing and Sculpting is published in conjunction with an exhibition of the same name organized by the Nasher Sculpture Center in cooperation with The Estate of David Smith. The exhibition is presented at the Nasher Sculpture Center, Dallas, Texas, from April 16 to July 17, 2005.

The exhibition is supported by funding from The Eugene McDermott Fund at the Nasher Sculpture Center and generous grants from the Roblee Foundation and Sotheby's.

Designed by 2x4, New York

Printed and bound by Transcontinental, Montréal, Québec

Edited by Fronia Simpson and Susan Cooke

Photo Captions
Cover: David Smith's hand with sketch for *Voltri I*, Voltri, Italy, 1962
p.2: Drawings laid out on the living room floor, Bolton, September 1959
p.3: David Smith, Voltri workshop, Italy, 1962.
pp.4-5, 6-7: David Smith in his drawing studio, Bolton, 1962.
pp.8-9: Sculpture fields, Bolton, 1962.
pp.10: *Anchorhead*, with wall painting, Bolton, 1952.
p.11: *Anchorhead*, with *Personnage Seeking Australia* in the background, Bolton, 1952.
pp.12, 13: *Cubi VIII*, Bolton, 1962.
pp.14-15: Sculpture fields, Bolton, ca. 1963.
p.16: *Voltri VI*, Spoleto, Italy, 1962.
p.17: David Smith with his assistants and *Voltri VI*, Voltri workshop, Italy, 1962.
p.18: David Smith (self-portrait) working on *Tanktotem IX*, Bolton, 1960.
p.19: Tanktotem IX, Bolton, 1960.
p.20-21: Sculpture fields, Bolton, 1963.
p.22: David Smith in his drawing studio, 1962.
p.29: Photograph of the floor of David Smith's Bolton studio, inscribed by the artist, 1959.
p.51: David Smith, Bolton, 1961.
p.56-57: David Smith seated on his terrace overlooking the upper field, Bolton, 1962.
p.136: *Voltri XVIII* (1962), Voltri, Italy, 1962.
p.148: Sculpture fields, Bolton, 1961. Photo by David Smith.
p.151: David Smith, drawing from a nude model, c. 1940.
p.162: David Smith welding *Voltri Bolton VIII* (1962), 1962.
p.168: David Smith, ca. 1962.
Back cover: David Smith in his office (self-portrait), Bolton, ca. 1953.

Photo Credits
Larry Berkow: p.77
Michael Bodycomb: p.138
Dan Budnick: pp.4-5,6-7,8-9,20-21,22,51,56-57,162
Michael Cavanagh and Kevin Montague: p.35
David Heald: pp.63,67,71,83,99,116,129
Tom Jenkins: p.127
Garnett McCoy: pp.14-15.
Robert McAfee: p.151
Robert McKeever/Gagosian Gallery: pp.59,61,64,68,69,73-75,78, 80,81,84-87,89-96,100,101,104-109,111-116,119-122, 124,125,129 133,137,140,141,144-147
Ugo Mulas: front cover, p.3,17
Jerry L. Thompson: p.142
David Smith: pp.2,10,11,12,13,16, 18,19,29,43 (fig.7),45,47, 136,148, back cover

Contents

Introduction

David Smith can justifiably be ranked as one of the great American draftsmen of the twentieth century. Yet his drawings have never received the international acknowledgment and appreciation accorded his sculpture. This blind spot in the criticism and collecting of modern art has persisted despite the efforts of museums and galleries, through exhibitions and catalogues, to introduce audiences to the considerable power, beauty, and importance of Smith's works on paper. I personally can remember vividly the sense of discovery and growing education that accompanied my visits to several gallery shows featuring Smith's drawings, and my wonder that his outstanding achievements in the medium had not attracted a wider following. It was partly out of a desire to help correct this situation, and partly to study the fascinating interaction of Smith's drawings and sculpture, that the present exhibition was organized.

Smith drew all of his life, and during the mature years of his career his output as a draftsman was immense. Among other great twentieth-century sculptors, Pablo Picasso demonstrated an analogously prolific and inventive devotion to drawing. Like Picasso, Smith enthusiastically explored different drawing techniques, media, and formats. He drew on scraps of paper, in notebooks, on large and expensive sheets, and even on the floor. Like Picasso, he drew as a way of life, for a host of reasons, including but certainly not limited to investigations of sculpture and sculptural ideas. Until we have a catalogue raisonné of Smith's drawings, the full range of his graphic output and thought, and his full achievement as an innovative draftsman, are difficult to grasp. At one point he reported that he was making three to four hundred large drawings a year, and while this number is exaggerated, it is not hyperbole to say that drawing provided the firm and lasting foundation of his art. In our exhibition and catalogue, we hope to elucidate this core relationship between drawing and sculpture and the ways that work in one medium supported and energized the other.

Many people deserve credit for the realization of this project, and the person at the top of that list is Raymond Nasher. The superb collection of sculpture that he and his late wife, Patsy, put together starting in the 1970s helped to inspire the exhibition, engendering the thought that a juxtaposition of the sculptures with related drawings would illuminate all the works and also cast light on Smith's working methods. The Nasher Sculpture Center, designed by Renzo Piano and built by Raymond Nasher as a home for the Nasher Collection and forum for major exhibitions and education programs focused on modern sculpture, provides an ideal laboratory to examine these interactions.

From its outset, this exhibition received the devoted and tireless support of Candida Smith, daughter of the artist and official co-curator of the show, and Peter Stevens, Executive Director of the David Smith Estate. These two colleagues, both leading experts on Smith's work, helped develop the premise of the exhibition, select its contents, and shape the catalogue. In addition to providing an insightful catalogue essay, Candida collaborated on the exhibition installation. Susan Cooke, Associate Director of the David Smith Estate, provided invaluable support especially with cataloguing the works in the show, arranging photography, contributing research materials to the catalogue, and helping to manage packing and shipping. Ealan Wingate of Gagosian Gallery very kindly lent design advice. I cannot thank enthusiastically enough these dedicated partners.

At the Nasher Sculpture Center, several staff members were instrumental in the organization and success of the show. Jed Morse, Assistant Curator, researched Smith's writings and statements on drawing for the catalogue and worked on exhibition planning and installation; Jennifer Ritchie Lawson, Registrar, managed loan agreements as well as arrangements for shipping, crating, and insurance; Joanna Rowntree, Conservator, worked on planning, installation, and condition reports; two successive Executive Assistants, Ginny Huntress and Amy Weatherford, oversaw exhibition correspondence and helped with manuscript preparation; Rachel Schulze, Assistant Curator of Education, organized various education programs; and Jane Offenbach, Director of Marketing and Development, managed public relations and special events. The New York graphic design firm 2x4 designed the exhibition catalogue with characteristic originality and elegance. The Gagosian Gallery generously provided exhibition photography, and Fronia W. Simpson edited the catalogue manuscript with sensitivity and many helpful suggestions.

Finally, we are especially indebted to those lenders who generously agreed to share their treasured works of art with our appreciative audiences. Chief among these are the officers of the David Smith Estate. Without the magnanimous cooperation of Candida and Rebecca Smith and Peter Stevens, our exhibition would not have been thinkable. Also crucial for the success of the project were important loans from Tony and Gail Ganz, Samuel and Ronnie Heyman, Susan and Larry Marx courtesy of Neal Meltzer Fine Art, Andrea Woodner, the Dallas Museum of Art, and the Meadows Museum at Southern Methodist University. For the latter two loans, we are greatly indebted to Dr. John Lane and Charles Wylie, Director and Curator of Contemporary Art, respectively, at the Dallas Museum of Art, and Dr. Edmund Pillsbury, Director of the Meadows Museum.

For all of her support over the years for the cause of David Smith drawings and for helping to open my own eyes to the importance and beauty of these works, I offer special thanks to Margo Leavin.

Steven Nash

The Importance of Drawing

Steven Nash

t paint white areas on the floor
ay out parts for relationships
fter arc-welding — sparks
molten balls and arc flares
leave images in negative
white and burnt traceries

there — become nature

David Smith's protean career single-handedly brought new maturity and international ambition to American sculpture. With hard-boiled individualism, he forged formal languages in iron and steel that incorporated historical and contemporary sources, mostly European, with an optimistic, even joyous, spirit of American construction. Today, forty years after his death, the body of work he created still astonishes in its variety, technical mastery, and brawny creative energy. So powerful is Smith's legacy as a sculptor, however, that other, highly accomplished aspects of his art exist in a shadowy realm of limited acknowledgment and investigation. His work as a photographer, for example, has only lately attracted the attention it deserves. A series of paintings he made of nudes late in life had to wait until just a few years ago to reemerge from the sidelines of formalist critical opprobrium to be reassessed. And his vast output of works on paper, so telling a record of his visual thought and so impressive on its own aesthetic grounds, is still to a large extent terra incognita. Since about 1980, a number of exhibitions have focused on Smith's works on paper, but the majority of his drawings remain unexhibited and unpublished.[1] Most important, we still do not have a very clear picture of what drawing meant to Smith and how it both supported and deviated from his sculptural output.

This exhibition, although relatively modest in scale, celebrates David Smith the draftsman and hopes to cast new light on its still too-little-understood subject. It assembles approximately fifty major drawings plus related paintings spanning the years from his growing maturity in the 1930s to his magisterial accomplishments late in life. It undertakes, on the one hand, a study of these works as independent and forceful objects, indicative of the wide range of Smith's drawing styles, his sources of influence, and his graphic development. It also proposes, moreover, to look at these works in relation to Smith's sculptures in the Nasher Collection, some sculptures borrowed from other owners, and several paintings to try to understand more fully the complicated ways in which his two- and three-dimensional works interrelate in dialogues of investigation and invention. This is a subject commonly raised in studies of Smith's work. "The interchange of techniques seems an incontrovertible condition of his art,"[2] for example, is a typical observation. But the interrogation of this interchange by examining specific examples has not yet been thoroughly pursued.

Smith himself stressed repeatedly the connectivity he felt between drawing and sculpture. All of his work, he allowed, flowed from one continuous, evolving stream, with no "separate provision" for two-dimensional versus three-dimensional expression, either in "concept" or "the mind's reaction to form."[3] Early in his career he often used preparatory drawings to plan sculptures visually and conceptually, and drawing also provided a means to see, think, and imagine beyond the practical confines of what it was possible to construct. As he put it, he made drawings "sometimes [for] what sculpture is, [and] sometimes what sculpture can never be."[4] Starting in the early 1950s, however, preparatory studies became less common, as drawings tended to link to sculptures, not in linear developmental sequences or direct, one-to-one relationships, but more often as clusters or constellations of graphic themes and notations exploring related ideas, forms, and motifs. Smith equated drawing with writing, implying an embrace of such linguistic processes as free association, abstract signing, and visual phrase making, and we see such methologies at work in his graphic experimentation.[5]

Still more fundamental to his art, however, was the merger he effected between drawing, painting, gesture, assemblage, and spontaneity into an integrated process of design and construction. In this way, the ethic of drawing informed the very act of making sculpture. Smith's sculpture, for example, might translate a concept from drawing or painting into three-dimensional form, preserving frontality and linearity and probing distinctions between pictorial and sculptural space. But even when this technique of "drawing in space" was not operative, Smith endeavored to keep alive through his cutting, joining, laying out, erecting, welding, and finishing of works the gestural qualities he cultivated in drawings and paintings, thereby producing solid and balanced constructions that nevertheless resist stasis and containment. While it is misleading to assert, as some critics have done, that Smith's vision was essentially that of a painter and draftsman,[6] it is difficult to overestimate the importance of painting and especially drawing in his creative life. As Smith put it, he did not recognize "the limits where painting ends and sculpture begins."[7]

As is well known, Smith started his career as a painter and worked strictly in painting and drawing before making his first tentative sculptures in 1932.

At the Art Students League in New York, where he studied from 1926 to 1931, the artist and teacher Jan Matulka was a notable influence, through both his own cubist-inspired modernism and his introducing Smith to broader modernist developments. Important, too, was Smith's work with the famous drawing instructor Kimon Nicolaides, who stressed that drawing was fundamental to all the arts and helped instill in Smith a love of drawing from the live model that stayed with him all his life.[8] Through art circles, Smith also came into the stimulating company of a talented and articulate trio of artists—John Graham, Stuart Davis, and Arshile Gorky—whose apostle-like advocacy of modernism led Willem de Kooning to label them "the three smartest guys on the scene."[9]

Smith's earliest drawings include nudes, landscapes, and still lifes, and have a studious and exploratory if somewhat labored quality. They show him learning his métier and absorbing what he found interesting in European modernism, known to him from various publications and exhibitions but also refracted through the lens of work by Matulka, Gorky, Davis, and Graham. Figures 1 and 2 show strong debts, for example, to Matulka's simplified cubism and Gorky's abstracted biomorphism. In terms of European sources, Smith was especially drawn to the biomorphic figuration of Pablo Picasso, Joan Miró, André Masson, and Henry Moore, synthetic cubism, and the psychic pictorial spaces of such surrealists as Giorgio di Chirico and Alberto Giacometti (especially in the latter's tabletop compositions).

Several drawings in the exhibition, including plate numbers 1 and 8 show these influences at work. By the time of these studies, Smith was thinking as a sculptor. Both images are conceived as sculptures, complete with bases, and while neither was directly translated into three-dimensional form, they do presage later sculptural formulations. The reclining figure with guitar absorbed into the body anticipates the conflation of torso and cannon found in *Perfidious Albion* (pl. no. 4),[10] and the linear morphology of the bodies in *Untitled* relates closely to the open spatial construction of *Head* of 1938 (pl. no. 6). Also, the liberal use of ink washes in the latter drawing shows a painterly approach to built form that manifests itself in the red coloration of *Head*. The two bodies in this image clearly derive from works by Picasso in his surrealist mode (e.g., fig. 3), while the narrative

FIG. 1
David Smith, *Untitled*, ca. 1930
Charcoal and pencil on paper
19½ x 12½ in. (49.5 x 31.8 cm)
The Estate of David Smith, New York

FIG. 2
David Smith, *Untitled*, 1934
Oil on canvas
35 x 40 in. (88.9 x 101.6 cm)
Jeffrey and Jacqueline Morby, Pittsburgh

space projected in the imagined sculpture comes directly from Giacometti. One can look ahead in Smith's oeuvre as far as *Anchorhead* of 1952 (pl. no. 35) and find a similar expression of rounded and linear bodily structure.

A crucial interlude in Smith's career not documented in our exhibition centers on his production of the vehemently antiwar bronzes *Medals for Dishonor*, together with a long series of drawings that explore similarly anguished imagery of war, brutality, death, and destruction. Emerging first about 1938–39 and obviously linked to Smith's strong feelings about the Spanish Civil War and World War II, these drawings (e.g., fig. 4) are anomalous within the full span of his graphic work by virtue of their tightly detailed, intensely worked figuration. As is often remarked, the sources for this graphic style lie mainly in Northern European drawings and engravings of the fifteenth and sixteenth centuries and also German expressionism, as Smith turned to gothicizing traditions as well as the dark visions of Francisco de Goya and Hieronymus Bosch in a search for a vehicle to express his personal despair and anger. A similarly horrific drawing, *Untitled (Desert Skeletons)*, appeared as early as 1936 as a signpost for what would soon appear in the Medals.[11]

From the early 1940s come several drawings in the exhibition (pl. nos. 2, 3 and 5) more indicative of extended trends in his development. *Pillar of Sunday* (pl. no. 2) is a study for one of Smith's best-known early sculptures (fig.5), a totemic structure of glyphlike, ideational forms similar to those in other works of the period including *Perfidious Albion* and *House in a Landscape* (pl. nos. 4 and 9). In the drawing, executed in a strongly penned but still loose and shorthand style, several of the glyphs are already attached to the central pillar, at least in vestigial form. But there is also a freewheeling experimentation with other motifs, especially several birds shown alternately as a bird of peace, an airplane-bird, and a phallic, winged cannon. The final sculpture evokes church and religion, possibly as a derisive comment by Smith on his mother's conventional religious beliefs (he referred to her as "the pillar of the church").[12] Symbols of love, books (probably scripture), peace, and the Holy Ghost all adorn the central pillar a bit like Christmas tree ornaments. Their loopy, rather cartoonish shapes show Smith "drawing" figurative forms with his torch, as he

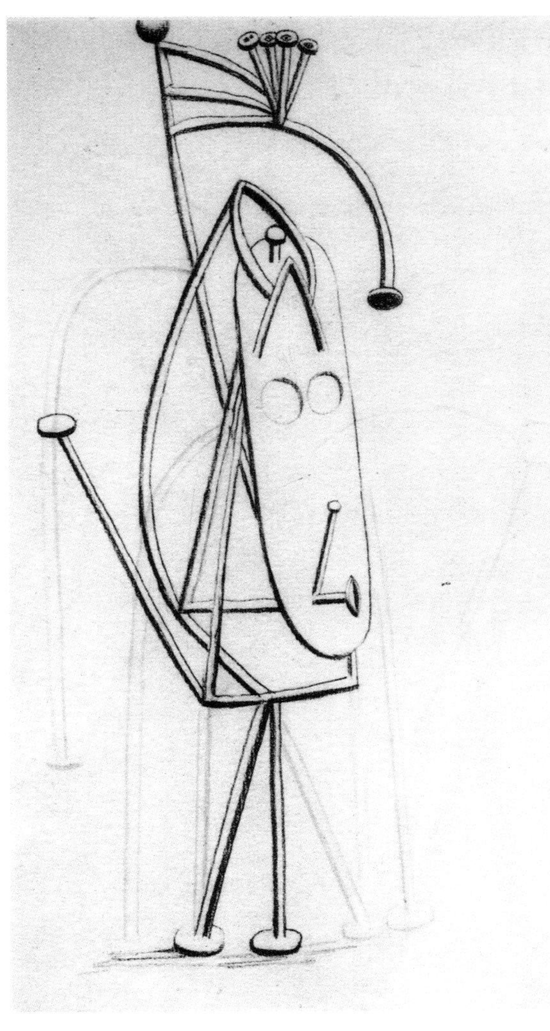

FIG. 3
Pablo Picasso, *Figure (Study for Sculpture)*, September 1927
Charcoal and pencil graphite on paper
12 x 9 1/8 in. (30.5 x 23.2 cm)
Musée Picasso, Paris

FIG. 4
David Smith, *Study for Medals for Dishonor*, 1938–39
Pen and ink wash on paper
16 x 20 in. (40.6 x 50.8 cm)
The Estate of David Smith, New York

FIG. 5
David Smith, *Pillar of Sunday*, 1945
Steel, painted pink
31 x 16 5/8 x 9 1/2 in. (78.7 x 42.2 x 24.1 cm)
Indiana University Art Museum

did also in *House in a Landscape* and other narrative, tabletop tableaux of the period clearly inspired by the theatrical spaces of surrealist paintings and sculpture.

In Smith's study for *Perfidious Albion* (pl. no. 3), a sculpture related to *Medals for Dishonor* in its caustic political commentary, he explored a number of fantastic creatures that look back again to Picasso's surrealist drawings of the late 1920s. Each "figure" is imagined as three-dimensionally modeled, with strongly drawn, rounded contours and a liberal application of shading. That is, they are envisioned as sculptures. Even in technique there is a remembrance of Picasso's bonelike creatures. The compositional studies for *Perfidious Albion* are particularly well developed, to the extent of showing both front and back views. In the sculpture, Smith reworked the torso of the figure, incorporating symbols of a cannon and interior anatomy onto the body, but the motifs hung from the figure's trident head—a shield or carapace or possibly rib cage and entrails—closely match those previewed in the frontal view as seen in the drawing.

With *Pillar of Sunday*, we encounter a prime example of Smith moving directly from drawing to sculpture and preserving in the process a relatively flat formal structure. This same tendency is seen over and again, and can be traced with particular clarity in the present exhibition with the sculpture *The Forest* from 1950 and the drawings that cluster around it (pl. nos. 13, 15, 16, 18, 19, 22, 23, and 24). These related drawings all postdate the sculpture, but others exist from the year *The Forest* was created.

Surveying these drawings, several salient characteristics stand out. Smith had moved by this point to a greater insistence on linear structure in his drawings, with less shading and less intention to produce a solid, weighty, space-displacing volume. Most of the works shown here feature landscape views or motifs distilled into basically flat webs of lines of varying thickness, but they are mostly thin and delicate. These seem to respond to specific features of landscape such as contours of hills and valleys, trees, the outlines of geological formations, and shadows. A clue to their morphology comes with ΔΣ *11/23/51 (Old Snow)* (pl. no. 22), which Smith indicated through its title was a view of a winter landscape.

Out of a landscape experience, Smith abstracted graphic patterns, still undoubtedly redolent for him of his own attachment to nature, that gradually take on new lives. Their strong black and white dynamics, the language of slicing, stabbed, nuanced, and thickened lines, and the allover, off-the-page compositions connect them to the paintings and drawings of the abstract expressionists, although they retain a very distinctive linear sensibility. This sensibility, one can posit, is innately sculptural. It might be going too far to say that Smith was already thinking of sculptures when he made such studies, but they share a basic organizational tendency that coalesces form into grills or screens of structure, which begin to suggest built shapes. Indeed, close parallels with some of these tense linear webs are found in Smith's Agricola sculptures of about 1952 (compare pl. nos. 17 and 21).

Similar affinities exist with *The Forest*. None of the drawings relates as closely to the sculpture as the one-to-one connection between *Hudson River Landscape* (pl. no. 14) and the famous sculpture of the same name, which is also part of this series of landscape investigations and was based on drawings Smith made while traveling by train up and down the Hudson River Valley. What is seen instead is a loose dialogue of motifs that moves from drawings to sculpture and back to drawings, recalling Smith's metaphor of his creative work as a continuous flowing stream.

The Forest, essentially a flat, frontal, painted sculpture that is read pictorially, it might seem, as a relief or even a painting, raises that key question: does the graphic vision dominate the sculptural? Certainly works such as *Hudson River Landscape*, *Australia*, and *The Banquet* (all from 1951)[13] are among the purest embodiments in modern sculpture of the concept of "drawing in space" inherited by Smith from Picasso and Julio González and capture the fluid rhythms, velocity, and changes of direction of a drawn line. But how completely do such works resemble or rely on a graphic paradigm? *The Forest* is a useful work to analyze in this regard. In this case, it appears to be a fairly seamless process through which Smith abstracted the natural landscape into flattened graphic patterns that fed directly into the idea of his sculpture. His incorporation of found objects for trees—the sawtoothed implements he used also in other sculptures—yielded an a priori flat structure that he played against the cutouts of birds and the stringy limbs of a figure hanging from one of the branches. Despite its planar composition, however, *The Forest* has a vibrant three-dimensional life. Forms are overlapped, layered, and bent, so that they must be viewed in the round to be fully understood. Patterns in the painting of the work vary between front and back. Details on the front do not always give hints as to what is on the back. And, inescapably, mark making in metal—cutting, bending, and welding—is spatial thought. The work may seem assertively flat and picturelike, but it still occupies space in a volumetric way and declares a muscular sensibility for three-dimensional form. Similarly, to look at *Hudson River Landscape* or *Australia* as flat and strictly frontal is to misunderstand Smith's genius for spatial manipulation and to fail to read the surrounding spaces as critical parts of the sculpture. It is, in fact, this transfer from drawing to sculpture that helps us see better the ways Smith constantly probed the differences between pictorial and sculptural space, including his consistent endowment of the latter with shape.

At the same time Smith was working on these landscape themes, he began a lengthy series of drawings of figural motifs in a variety of stylistic modes. Shallow line-ups of vertical totemlike figures are depicted in loose brushstrokes of ink and wash (pl. nos. 29, 30 and 31), sharply drawn strokes of the pen (pl. no. 34), and combinations of pen and brush (pl. no. 33). Sometimes the figures are abstracted into rows of calligraphic columns (pl. nos. 39 and 40), and at others are turned horizontally and stacked up, with bodies morphing into landscape vistas (pl. nos. 27 and 28).

These works correspond most closely within Smith's sculptural oeuvre to the Tanktotem series and other standing, constructed "figures" from the same time. Rarely do we find a drawing that closely prefigures a sculpture, but many cases occur of close family relationships. Compare the drawings ΔΣ *9/4/52* and *Untitled* (pl. nos. 33 and 34) to *Tanktotem IX* and *Anchorhead* (pl. no. 49 and 35). The composition of *Tower Eight* (pl. no. 32) is hinted at strongly in ΔΣ *10/31/54 3* (pl. no. 45), confirming the figurative genealogy of that sculpture, which is also adumbrated by a spray painting from 1957, *Untitled* (fig. 6). All three of these works mark an important moment in Smith's development.

FIG. 6
David Smith, *Untitled*, 1957
Spray enamel and oil on canvas
46 1/2 x 11 1/4 in. (118.1 x 28.6 cm)
Aaron I. Fleischman Collection

The drawing and painting—this was Smith's first documented spray painting[14]—show the advent of a compositional type new for him, which was then given physical reality in the sculpture. Compared with the earlier Tanktotems and other standing figural works, *Tower Eight* has a totally linear structure devoid of mass or solid planes, fully materializing again the idea of making a spatial drawing with metal and discarding completely the surrealist influences that still inhabit the Tanktotem drawings and sculptures. It is an utterly open, transparent structure with no single, prescribed angle for viewing. Realized at first in the relatively modest scale of *Tower Eight*, these same principles were later expanded by Smith in the gracefully tall *Tower I* of 1963, a stainless steel composition 23½ feet high.[15] Furthermore, *Tower Eight* is one of a handful of works Smith made in the 1950s in silver, a first step toward the polished, reflective, stainless steel surfaces so critical to the Cubi series of the 1960s and its embrace of dazzling light and reflections of sky into the body of the sculptures.

Some of these figural drawings are hasty studies, obviously penned very quickly. Others, such as ΔΣ *9/4/52* (pl. no.33), are more carefully drawn and finished but maintain a light touch, both in the fluid work of the pen and the light application of wash. All of the studies seem to be done alla prima, that is, in one effort, without adjustments or underdrawing, and with a lack of interest in high degrees of finish. Some, such as *Untitled*, ΔΣ *10-9-57* and *Untitled* (pl. nos. 29, 30 and 39), which may seem a little like doodles, are actually quite subtle. These works show vertical totems pushed together as if they were in an ethnographic display case. They are atavistic, arrested in a process of development or decay or caught in stages of mutation. As depicted, however, Smith coaxed quite an intriguing variety of bodily types out of his limited graphic vocabulary. Some forms seem skeletal, some more fleshed-out and human, and others more animal, while some are subsumed in an abstracting geometry. One cannot help but feel a certain humor and playfulness—definitely a part of Smith's complex personality and work—in his tweaking of our imaginations. The idea of an alphabet of recombinant motifs is also vividly illustrated in some of these drawings where, for example, a nude may become a constructivist tower and then a pillar of brushy accents.

It is also worth noting that none of the drawings reviewed shows the forceful "carving" or inscription of contours or the turning of a form in different perspectives sometimes found in sculptors' drawings in the preparation of a plan or blueprint for a sculpture. Many of the outlines are sketchy or feathered, allowing surrounding space to infiltrate the form. Emphasis is self-consciously placed on light touch rather than schematic pattern, showing that Smith cared about the drawings as drawings. The arrangement of motifs in shallow registers, reminiscent of many of Henry Moore's drawings, signals an artist used to working with discrete, tangible forms. But drawing generally meant something much different from a warmup for sculpture.

The loose, Asian-inspired brushwork seen selectively in several of these works led to a more sustained series of brush and ink drawings from the late 1950s and early 1960s marked by a distinctive energy and expansiveness of execution. Smith's enthusiasm for this genre of drawing carried over to mixing his own pigments; for example, he favored a concoction of egg yolk, India ink, and gouache. These works in general tend toward abstraction, although many, such as *Untitled* and *Untitled (5/3/59)* (pl. nos. 36 and 37), retain a landscape bias and others show traces of the nude figure. Two works shown here from 1962 entitled *Voltri 3,* and *Untitled*, with their dense weavings of brushed lines and massed blacks (pl. nos. 54 and 53), may seem at first to be nonobjective but actually were Smith's responses to the hilly coastal landscape at Voltri, Italy, where he worked for a month in 1962 in an old steel factory in preparation for an exhibition at the Spoleto Festival that summer.

Several famous photographs from the early 1960s show Smith's studio and living room at Bolton Landing with the floors covered by abstract brush drawings. One of these photographs (fig. 7) he inscribed, "living room floor/studio in house also this time both floors full/sometimes I draw for days/I like it/and it's a balance with the labor of sculpture/to average a drawing for every day I live/some form of identity." In these works, the spontaneity and dynamism of the brushwork in earlier drawings of figural and landscape motifs take on an independent life, with strong cadences of thick, dashing lines obliterating any reference to nature. Dense screens of choppy, churning forms emerge, some of them almost completely solid (e.g., fig. 8). Figure is not distinct from ground; instead, strokes merge with the paper, energize it, and create a deep space, with different tones and sheens of pigment sometimes used to increase the depth of space between strokes. These works bring Smith's drawings particularly close to moments in drawings by abstract expressionist artists he admired such as Franz Kline, Willem de Kooning, and Jackson Pollock. Not delicate, elegant drawings, with the smooth wrist action of Chinese calligraphers, they are aggressive works in their energetic attack of the paper and seem again to suggest the hand of a sculptor in the brusque push and pull of the brush and heavy overlays of ink, creating powerful forces of negative and positive space. In reviewing them, one can almost hear the voice of the artist as he instructed his daughters in drawing: "Feel your body and its actual movement. Draw from deep inside... Wait for the disciplined reception of the inner impulse... Be bold."[16]

Could these abstract drawings with brushy forms floating in space have any relationship to Smith's sculptures? In some cases, such as *XLII* (pl. no. 51), the forms separate into more sculptural alignments, which in this particular instance anticipate in composition the drawing ΔΣ-*Jan 1962* (pl. no. 58), that either prefigures or is closely based on Smith's painted steel sculpture *Primo Piano I* of 1962 (fig. 9). At other times (e.g., fig. 8), the dense weaving of strokes into an almost solid screen with small areas of spatial penetration brings to mind Smith's work in Voltri with solid sheets of rolled steel welded into place as flat planes, as seen in *Voltri VI* (pl. no. 55). In this work, a stripe of space divides the two powerful upright plates, allowing light to penetrate and providing a greater sense of visual depth that relieves the compositional weight of the sculpture. A similar role is played by the small windows of space within the blackness of the ink drawings. The thick lines in other works have a structural quality not unlike the architectonic substructures in Kline's brush drawings, and we can see, perhaps, a relationship between the heft and stacking or overlay of such lines and the play of dense, heavy forms in a sculpture such as *Voltri XVIII* (pl. no. 63).

Smith continued to make calligraphic brush drawings until 1962 and occasionally later. It was a genre he clearly relished, producing hundreds of works in medium and large formats. As early as 1958–59, however, he had

FIG. 7
Photograph of David Smith's living room with drawings laid out on the floor, Bolton Landing; photograph inscribed by Smith, 1962

FIG. 8
David Smith, *6/30/3-58*, 1958
Egg ink on paper
17 x 21 in. (43.2 x 53.3 cm)
The Estate of David Smith, New York

pioneered a radically different series of drawings and paintings, one more closely linked to his sculptures and more popularly associated with his name. Referred to collectively as the sprays, he made works in this mode until his death. Their emergence in this period and their use of interconnected geometric forms occurred more or less simultaneously with Smith's shift to a highly geometric mode of standing, relieflike sculpture, with such works as *XI Books III Apples* from 1959.[17] It is hard to determine if the drawings actually preceded the related sculptures, but if they did, they would constitute another example of Smith's drawings setting forth new problems and initiating new directions that soon affected his sculpture as well.

Smith's famous spray drawings (pl. nos. 58 and 61) were made by placing various cutout shapes on a sheet of paper and spraying over them with different colors of enamel paint. Removing the cutouts revealed designs of unpigmented white forms. Although they actually are negative spaces, they take on a strongly positive role. Smith sometimes reinforced these empty spaces with strokes of white gouache, giving them palpable body. The sprayed passages feature lovely, cloudy textures of color, which play against the negative/positive whites and the geometric forms, producing a spectral quality that calls to mind the photographic Rayograms of Man Ray. The buildup of droplets of paint, however, creates on the paper a highly tactile, metallic surface that begins to suggest a sense of actual metal, again closing the distance between drawing and sculpture.

Part of the intrigue and power of these works derives from the fact that they represent solid, sculptural form in such an ephemeral atmosphere. The shapes are often out of focus, definite yet indefinite, sculptural and painterly at the same time, a perfect amalgam of contrasting sensibilities. Many of them are what Smith described as drawings of sculptures that "can never be,"[18] meaning in this case, gestural and disembodied compositions of floating masses, as seen in plate numbers 50 and 59 and again in the spray paintings such as plate numbers 47 and 48. These are freely inventive works that show Smith looking for vivid painterly effects rather than sculptural relationships. Others are more constructivist and either closely resemble actual sculptures or posit highly buildable compositions. In the former category

FIG. 9
David Smith, *Primo Piano I*, 1962
Steel painted white
110 x 144 x 21 in. (279.4 x 365.8 x 53.3 cm)
Private Collection

is plate number 58, which relates directly, as already noted, to *Primo Piano I* (fig. 9). In the latter are plate number 61, which has affinities with *Cubi V*,[19] plate number 65, which shares structural elements with *Cubi XXI*,[20] and plate number 60. Considering the structural nature of these compositions and ties to actual sculptures, we have to ask whether Smith ever used such drawings as preparatory studies. Some may have played suggestive roles in the generation of built sculptures, although we know from photographs that Smith often worked out the precise structures in his Cubi series using cardboard boxes to build maquettes. And it is likely that spray drawings relating closely to sculptures came after and not before them. But as a whole, these works illustrate again the interchange between media so basic to Smith's art.

There is even a correspondence between the means that Smith used to produce these drawings and the way he laid out some of his sculptures. Commonly reproduced photographs of Smith's studio show white rectangles he painted on the floor in order to see more clearly the composition of metal parts that he placed on top of them (fig. 10). He manipulated the parts until he found a pleasing structure, in a sense "drawing" or "collaging" with them on the white ground of the floor. Sometimes he made an actual drawing in chalk or charcoal, sketching a sculpture's base on the floor, for example. The whole process allowed him to transfer into work with metal the spontaneity he so appreciated in drawing. Furthermore, he noted that when he welded his pieces together, the sparks and burns that attacked the white grounds on the floor reminded him of his spray technique in drawing and painting, another aspect of gestural and pictorial elements entering his sculpture.

A final and fascinating chapter in Smith's development as a draftsman was cut short midstream by his tragically early death in 1965. He had worked with nude models earlier for sketches and photographs, but in 1962 he began a concerted series of paintings, drawings, and photographs of the nude that constitutes a major body of work, one that for a long time raised critical hackles for its seeming abandonment to conservative figuration (see pl. nos. 68 and 70). Parallels are sometimes apparent with the late black-and-white drip paintings by Jackson Pollock, both through certain similarities of technique and a reversion to figurative allusions that evinced confused if not openly hostile responses.

FIG. 10
David Smith's studio with white rectangles painted on the floor, Bolton Landing house, 1962

Smith's drawings and paintings of nudes were sometimes done with a loose brush technique that looks back to his landscape brush drawings of the 1950s and early 1960s, and many with syringes filled with ink or paint and long brushes, all to facilitate the dripped, poured, and calligraphically looping lines that he favored. Although such works may seem, at least in terms of subject matter, to depart from Smith's contemporaneous work with stainless steel geometric sculpture, Brooks Adams has written persuasively about their sculptural attributes:

> The black enamel paint that defines Smith's figures... has an emphatically physical quality that evokes forged iron.... The pooling, flowing, and congealing enamel on these canvases conveys a low-relief sculptural presence, and the concomitant impression of mutating forms parallels the experience of looking at sculpture in the round—not least Smith's own late sculptures, with their simultaneous broadness and thinness, and their alternately frontal and slivered perspectives.[21]

It can be added that sometimes the flattened compositions of lines flowing around open centers that Smith produced in these paintings point back with fascinating similarity to such early sculptures as *Hudson River Landscape* and *Australia*.[22]

We wonder where these works would have led in Smith's oeuvre, had he had more time. Possibly to more open, linear, and openly figurative sculptures? What is certain is that the force of invention and commitment behind them would not have played out quickly.

Smith had noted famously that he appreciated the physical and mental relief that drawing provided in contrast to the more laborious task of building sculptures. Drawing was particularly critical, he said, "for the sculptor, who, of necessity, works in media slow to take realization. And where the original creative impetus must be maintained during labor, drawing is the fast-moving search which keeps physical labor in balance."[23] Other levels of meaning, however, are also confided here, concerning the importance of gesture and spontaneity. Smith drew all the time and for a host of reasons: to jot down observations, test ideas, resolve problems, plot a sculpture, explore a technique, relax, make something beautiful. What he drew often had very little direct connection with concurrent sculptures. But even when these formal relationships were distant, drawing helped him stay fresh and keep alive the pulse of instinct that he loved about drawing and painting and always sought to instill into sculpture.[24] What he abhorred most in sculpture was dead, static form. When we think of all the methodologies he used to combat this morbidity—flowing lines in space, painted and burnished surfaces, evacuated interiors, risky courting of imbalance, pronounced two-sidedness, intimations of mutation, and so forth—we feel the life force in his work and the profound meaning he attached to drawing as a wellspring for that force.[25] As we have seen, Smith's drawings, like his sculptures, do not fit into stereotypical stylistic categories or follow a linear path of development. They plot his movement away from formative influences into distinctly personal modes of expression, frequently mark changes of direction basic to his art in general, and most important, seem as natural to his life as breath itself. They provided a constant declaration of independence, as did his sculptures. Smith's own words, in a previously quoted statement that reads as a personal poem, perhaps best summarize his investment in drawing: "To average a drawing for every day I live/some form of identity."[26]

Notes

1 The main exhibitions and catalogues to focus on David Smith's drawings include Paul Cummings, *David Smith: The Drawings*, exh. cat. (New York: Whitney Museum of American Art, 1979); Edward F. Fry and Miranda McClintic, *David Smith: Painter Sculptor Draftsman*, exh. cat. (New York: George Braziller; Washington, D.C.: Hirshhorn Museum and Sculpture Garden, 1982); Trinkett Clark, *The Drawings of David Smith*, exh. cat. (Washington, D.C.: International Exhibitions Foundation, 1985); Jörn Merkert, ed., *David Smith: Sculpture and Drawings*, exh. cat. (Munich: Prestel-Verlag; London: Whitechapel Art Gallery, 1986); Magdalena Dabrowski, *David Smith: Related Clues*, exh. cat. (New York: Gagosian Gallery, 2004); and Alain Kirili, *David Smith: Draughtsman. Between Eros and Thanatos*, exh. cat. (Valencia: IVAM, 2004).

2 Consuelo Ciscar, in Kirili 2004, 11.

3 Smith, a lecture on the teaching of sculpture given at the Midwestern University Art Conference, Louisville, Kentucky, October 27, 1950. See Garnett McCoy, ed., *David Smith* (New York: Praeger Publishers, 1973), 64.

4 Smith, a lecture given in Portland, Oregon, March 23, 1953. See Cleve Gray, ed., *David Smith by David Smith: Sculpture and Writings* (New York: Thames and Hudson, 1988), 104.

5 Smith indicated to Thomas Hess in an interview in June 1964 that he did not "differentiate between writing and drawing." In "The Secret Letter," *David Smith*, exh. cat. (New York: Marlborough-Gerson Gallery, 1964), n.p.

6 See, for example, McClintic, in Fry and McClintic 1982, 38.

7 Smith, a paper delivered in the symposium "The New Sculpture," The Museum of Modern Art, New York, February 21, 1952; quoted in McCoy 1973, 82.

8 Smith's debts to Nicolaides are touched on by Phyllis Tuchman in *David Smith: Works on Paper 1953-1961*, exh. cat. (New York: Salander-O'Reilly Galleries, 1991), introduction.

9 Quoted in Mark Stevens and Annalyn Swan, *de Kooning: An American Master* (New York: Alfred A. Knopf, 2004), 93.

10 For a version of this nude, possibly related to a sculpture entitled *Reliquary House* from 1945, see Rosalind Krauss, *Terminal Iron Works: The Sculpture of David Smith* (Cambridge, Mass., and London: MIT Press, 1971), figs. 107–8, 132 n. 15. It may relate more directly to a stone sculpture from ca. 1943 entitled *Hope Chest*. See Rosalind Krauss, *The Sculpture of David Smith: A Catalogue Raisonné* (New York and London: Garland Publishing, 1977), fig. 157.

11 This drawing is reproduced in Fry and McClintic 1982, 52, cat. no. 9.

12 Krauss 1971, 96 n. 46.

13 These works are reproduced in Krauss 1971, pls. 60, 69, and 64.

14 Information provided by the David Smith Estate to the present owner of this painting indicates that "it is the first example documented in the artist's Estate to have been created in the then new medium of canned commercial spray enamel that became central to Smith's process and production during the 1950s."

15 See Candida Smith et al., *The Fields of David Smith*, exh. cat. (Mountainville, N.Y.: Storm King Art Center, 1999), 129.

16 Candida Smith, in Kirili 2004, 13.

17 Candida Smith, in Smith 1999, 68.

18 See note 4 above.

19 Candida Smith, in Smith 1999, 133.

20 Gray 1988, 159.

21 In Brooks Adams, *David Smith: The Last Nudes*, exh. cat. (New York: Gagosian Gallery, 2000), 9.

22 Compare, for example, *Untitled*, 1964 (Dabrowski 2004, no. 57) to *Hudson River Landscape* (Krauss 1971, pl. 60). I am indebted to Peter Stevens for pointing out these relationships to me.

23 Smith, a lecture delivered at Sophie Newcombe College, Tulane University, New Orleans, March 21, 1955. See McCoy 1973, 137.

24 Alain Kirili discusses the simultaneity of drawing, gesture, color, and spontaneity as forces within Smith's sculpture in Kirili 2004, 28–29.

25 In notes for his lecture at Sophie Newcombe College, Tulane University, on March 21, 1955, Smith wrote: "Drawings are usually not pompous enough to be called works of art. They are often too truthful. Their appreciation neglected, drawings remain the life force of the artist." McCoy 1973, 137.

26 See the inscription on the photograph reproduced in fig. 7.

Standing in the Landscape

Candida Smith

Standing in his landscape, watching his sculptures, David Smith was planted firmly in his artistic identity. As I knew him, a mature artist surrounded by his prodigious output in our ever-growing sculpture fields at Bolton Landing, my father had integrated his soul with his mountains. At our home in the Adirondacks, nature and the artist's nature merged fully.

David Smith chose his landscape early in life and committed to it as absolutely as he committed to his artwork. It became part of his identity, his inner life and creative process for the rest of his life.

David Smith was born and raised in the flat Midwestern plains of eastern Indiana and Ohio. After a short time in art school in New York City, he and his first wife spent a summer visiting friends in Bolton Landing, a small town on the edge of Lake George in the Adirondack Mountains. At the age of twenty-three, this struggling art student decided to buy a seventy seven-acre abandoned fox farm. He received a mortgage to buy a few weeks before the stock market collapse of 1929.

I am amazed by the audacity of my father at that moment. I imagine him recognizing a resonance within his own nature to these rough, rocky, iron-cored mountains, with their distant views of lake and sky. The ever-pouring narratives of the clouds, the almost overwhelming poetry of the place, imbued with a toughness and sadness from the hard living of the people of these mountains, pulled at him and called to him to plant himself in the drama of this landscape.

The Adirondacks are said to be the world's oldest mountain range. Geologically, the Rocky Mountains are much younger. The glaciers of the last Ice Age invaded these mountains, then taller than the Himalayas, roiled, condensed and split them, cutting glacial lakes throughout. The rich, rolling hills of New England seem sleepily domestic in comparison. Even the relatively level fields and meadows between the mountains seem to be creased by strain like my father's work pants.

I believe my father recognized an iron-cored endurance in those mountains which echoed his own. Open swaths of sky were broad enough for him to release his dreams upward. He felt more free here than anywhere else. The tough, enduring quality of Bolton's mountainscape could accept all of his intensity and not break. What a relief after a Midwestern Victorian home and the tight quarters of his

Brooklyn apartment. He didn't need to worry about breaking rules rules, igniting a fire from stray sparks or hemorrhaging his creative force in late-night art talk. Up in the country, he could work on his own and not be bothered.

David Smith was by no means a landscape artist—he would have bellowed at the thought—the Adirondack landscape became imbedded into his creative process and vocabulary. Rather than representing the outer contours of the mountains and woods, his work was informed by an intimacy of experiences. The fecund smell of spring rot, the lush loft of a full summer moss, the rough/soft tooth of lichen where it grew on a glacier-bared rock face, the muscle-feather flurry of a raven's takeoff were all aesthetically suggestive to him. They enriched the dreams and visions from which he made his art.

His house on the mountain was his home through two marriages, the birth of two daughters and their temporary absence after his second divorce. Of the nearly forty years there, too many were spent alone. Loneliness added another dimension to his view. During these years, as well as building his house and sculpture shop, he impacted his surroundings magnificently. He placed sculptures on marble blocks around the terrace of the house. The sculptures grew larger and began to enter the twenty acres of fields around the house [the art took root in the landscape]. The sculptures became monumental in scale and often heroic in tone. Some, like *Tanktotem IX* (pl. no. 49), stepped along like birds—on tripod legs. Others, like *Cubi II* (1963, pl. no. 67), stood resolute in totemic purity, center of gravity low and rising out of the earth. It was as if the landscape described in *House in a Landscape* (pl. no. 9), and *The Forest* (pl. no. 13), had been realized on his fields. In these sculptures the trees become sculptures, and become figures in his poetic transposition, one association sliding into another in a process of metaphorical flux. Sometimes he called our home a tree farm and sometimes a sculpture farm. These masses of sculptures in the fields, seventy-eight at the time of his death, stood in this dynamic process, giving the effect of holding a conversation among themselves and with the viewer. It felt very much like a performance of sculpture. Listening to his landscape opened the ear of the artist in David Smith with which he made the music of sculptures sounding and listening to each other.

David Smith liked to group his images to study them in combination, in a drawing, in the sculpture fields or for photography. We see *Perfidious Albion* (pl. no. 4) in physical form and drawn along with other sculptural images so that the artist could sense them together as a phrase. *Pillar of Sunday* (pl. no. 2) and *Untitled* (pl. no. 5) are also early examples. Throughout his life, Smith gathered groups of sculptures and arranged them together at great strain and effort for the sole purpose of a photograph. It might take days to pour the concrete pedestal bases into the ground, maneuver large, heavy sculptures in the back of the truck and set them up. After the photos were made, he put the art back. This looking and listening to the works together was a vital part of Smith's creative process. This grouping of images on the page, in a photo or aligned in the fields continued to the end of his life.

My father loved to walk in the woods. Taking great strides, he would lead us, telling stories of the Mohicans who might have made the trails we followed. My sister and I would try to walk as silently as they. Once, to my surprise and awe, we found the skull of a horse. How did it die there in the woods? We found bird bones, which often found their way into my father's "bone paintings," where bones from lunch or foraged in the woods were fixed on wooden mounts with pieces of a wheel or weeds by thick layers of paint. To me they were like stories carried down from another era, altered and fresh but with their raw, mythic magic underneath. When Becca and I were not around, he liked to collect and cook wild mushrooms. We had charts of edible and poisonous mushrooms on our bedroom wall, but I think he felt that was too dangerous for children. We ate only puffballs: round softball-sized mushrooms that sprout in a matter of hours after a soaking rain. We found raspberry and blackberry bushes in the small clearings that salamanders liked to frequent. Sometimes, my father would push down a dead tree with solemn intensity. He was protecting the thriving trees from a sudden crash and helping the enriching decay process get started. I still hear the crack-whoosh-boom in my imagination.

How little I know—until I see what happened in the night on the snow—the movement of animals, their paths, and why—the animals that fly the night birds leave no tracks except on the mind the star tracks that angle to earth sharp and direct the broad brushing of the wind shown only by the snow plops from branches circuling the bushes and tree.

This poem reveals much of my father's personal art view. His urgent interest in the events of nature such as cuneiform-like passages of bird feet across the snow spoke to him deeply, an abstract language speaking to the artist. Melded with his environment, he felt tracks of unseen birds in the night sky. Shooting stars make powerful lines and the wind makes broad strokes, as the artist does. Nature impacted my father's creative mind. Star tracks leave an after-image, as does the wind when it drops snow from branches.

His intentional spelling of the word "circuling" brings to mind his enormous admiration for James Joyce who often transposed word parts to make a new association. As Joyce opened language to the abstract association of word, sound and image, David Smith allowed his imagination to follow. Circuling, I believe, is an associative combination of circling and culling (as in selecting) and perhaps circumnavigating. The fallen bits of snow go around the bushes and the trees in such a way that they describe the shape and strength of the trees as well as forming a circle on the snow. Reading Joyce as an artist would, as opposed to a scholar, layers image upon association. The process leads the reader away from a normal narrative path toward an experience of layered sound and visual letter combinations that describes the contours of the deepest mind. Joyce freed words from literary tradition as Smith worked to free himself of artistic convention.

My father used to tell his friend Irving Sandler, the great art historian, "I didn't need Picasso, because I had Joyce." There was a twinkle in his eye when he said it. In his irreverent way, he meant that with this dynamic process of associative abstraction (rather than analytic abstraction) Joyce was opening a different door to modernism.

Imagine in the mind's eye, the animal tracks from the poem. See the broad brush of wind and sharp lines of star tracks and flights of birds. This is the most accurate description I have seen anywhere of my father's body of drawings. The eidetic imprint or after-image of these natural events is what we see on paper. His hand retraced these paths.

I retain an after-image of my father in the lower field standing among his sculpture. He is as integrated into the landscape as the cant of hill and the stands of pine, birch and maple. His gaze is lowered in thought, his left hand covering part of his mustache and bottom lip. Even though the fields are nearly barren of sculpture today, the after-image of his identity, his defiance, his extravagantly generous creativity is still standing in the landscape.

Candida Smith, January 2005, Bolton Landing

Plates

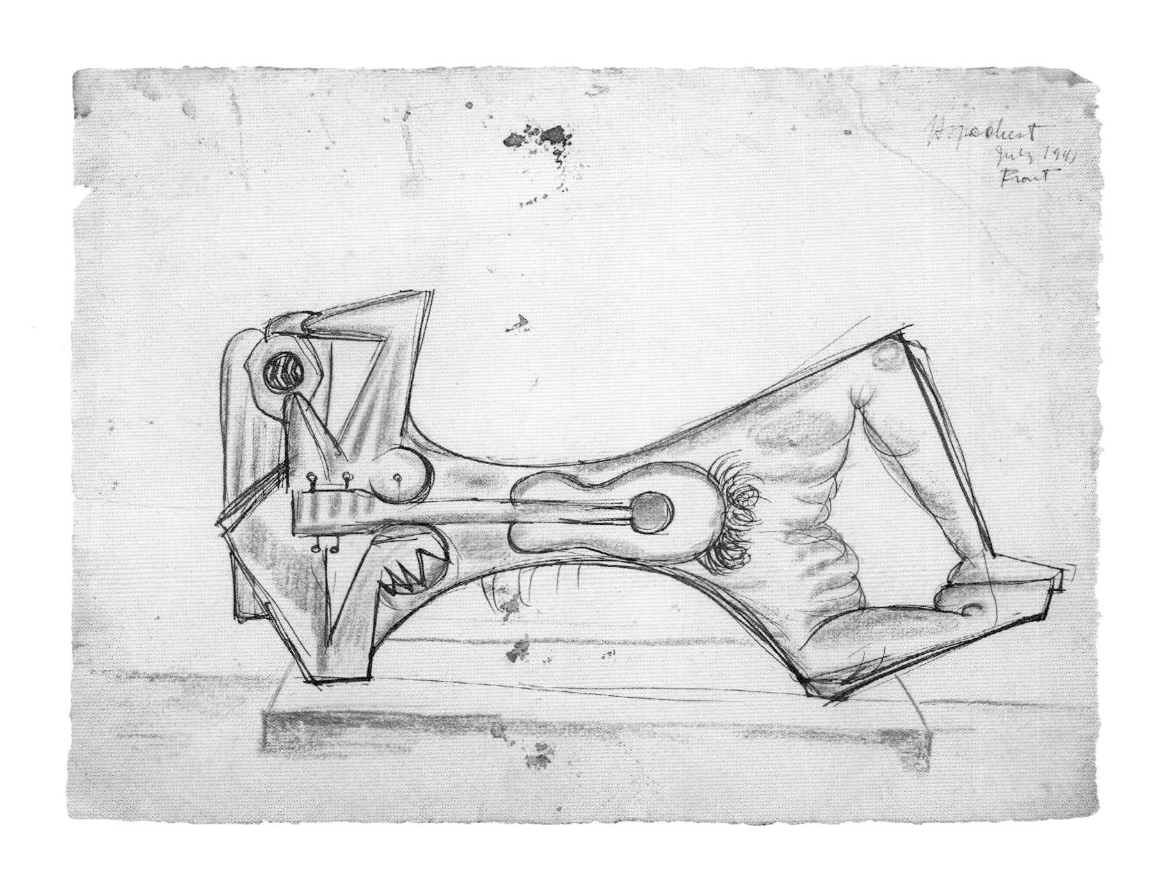

1
Hope Chest, 1941
Pen and ink and pastel on paper
$8\frac{5}{8} \times 11\frac{1}{2}$ in. (21.9 x 29.2 cm)
The Estate of David Smith

2
Pillar of Sunday, 1945
Ink, ink wash and pencil on paper
10 x 7 1/4 in. (25.4 x 18.4 cm)
The Estate of David Smith

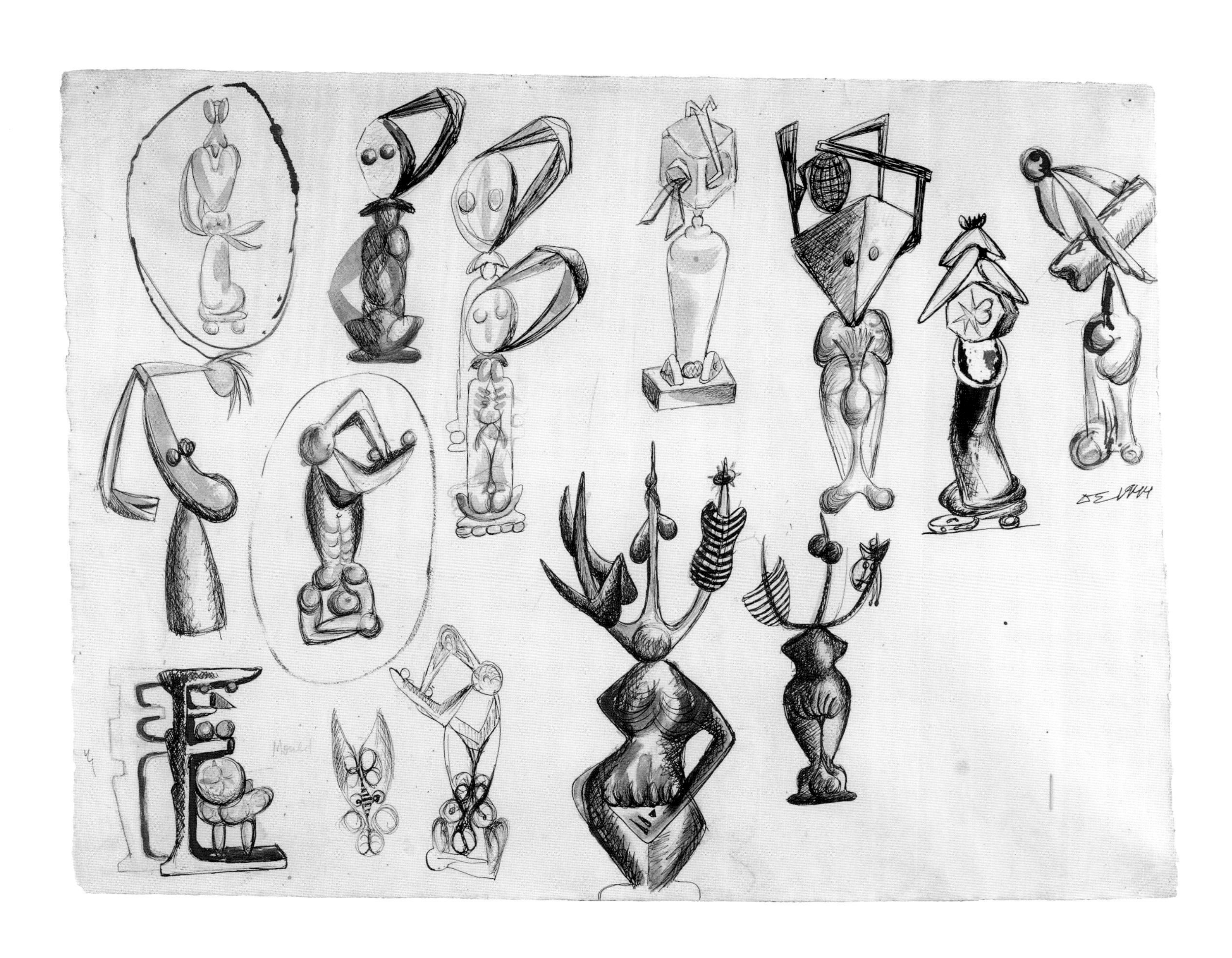

3
Untitled (*Sketches for Sculptures*), 1944
Pen and ink, gouache and pencil on paper
19⅝ x 25⅛ in. (49.8 x 63.8 cm)
The Estate of David Smith

4
Perfidious Albion (The British Empire), 1945
Bronze, cast iron, with patina
$14\frac{3}{8} \times 4\frac{1}{2} \times 2\frac{5}{8}$ in. (36.5 x 11.4 x 6.7 cm)
Raymond and Patsy Nasher Collection

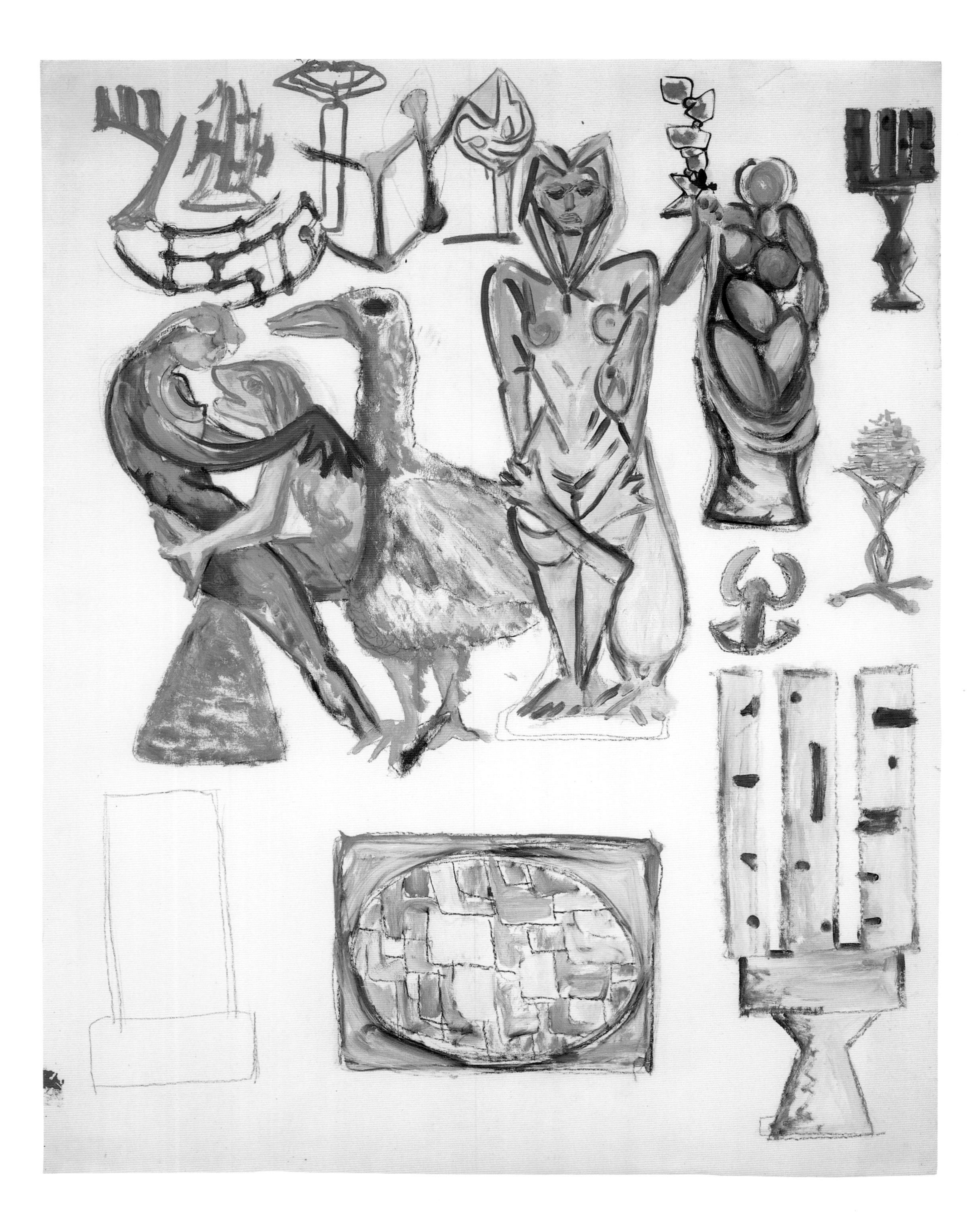

5
Untitled, 1946
Gouache and conte crayon on paper
29 x 22⅞ in. (73.7 x 58.1 cm)
The Estate of David Smith

6

Head, 1938
Welded iron, painted, on wood base
$17\frac{7}{16}$ x 8 x 7 in. (44.3 x 20.3 x 17.8 cm)
Raymond and Patsy Nasher Collection

7
Untitled (Two Bony Figures), 1946
Oil on cardboard
23¼ x 30 in. (59.1 x 76.2 cm)
The Estate of David Smith

8
Untitled, 1936–37
Black ink and wash on paper
17 x 22 in. (43.2 x 55.9 cm)
The Estate of David Smith

9
House in a Landscape (Rural Landscape with Manless House), 1945
Steel
18½ x 24¾ x 6 in. (47 x 62.9 x 15.2 cm)
Raymond and Patsy Nasher Collection

10
Untitled, 1946
Oil and tempera on paper
30 x 22 in. (76.2 x 55.9 cm)
The Estate of David Smith

11
Beach Scene, 1949
Oil pastel on paper
20¼ x 26 in. (51.4 x 66 cm)
The Estate of David Smith

12
Untitled, 1951
Egg ink, pencil and tempera on paper
17 x 22¼ in. (43.2 x 56.5 cm)
The Estate of David Smith

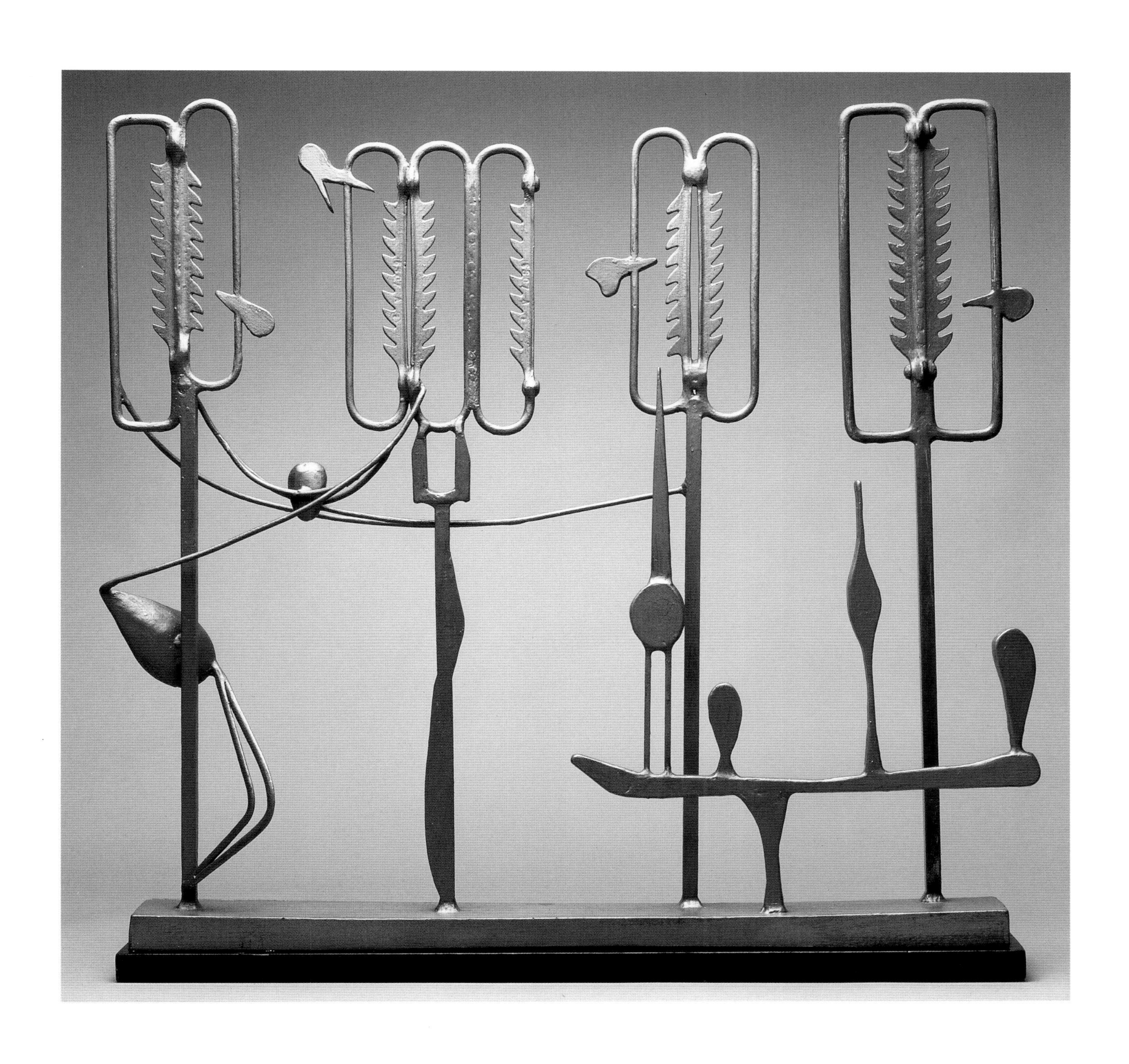

13
The Forest, 1950
Steel, painted, on wood base
38¼ x 39 x 4 in. (97.2 x 99.1 x 10.2 cm)
Raymond and Patsy Nasher Collection

1951

14
Hudson River Landscape, 1951
Egg ink, ink and tempera on paper
20 x 26 in. (50.8 x 66 cm)
The Estate of David Smith

15
ΔΣ *1/31/52*, 1952
Egg ink on paper
15 1/2 x 20 1/8 in. (39.4 x 51.1 cm)
Susan and Larry Marx, Courtesy of Neal Meltzer Fine Art, New York

16
Untitled, 1951
Ink and tempera on paper
19⅞ x 26 in. (50.5 x 66 cm)
The Estate of David Smith

17
Untitled (Agricola) also called *9/15/53*, 1953
Steel on iron base
21 1/2 x 37 3/4 x 13 in. (54.6 x 95.9 x 33 cm)
The Nasher Collection

18
Untitled, 1952
Egg ink and ink on paper
15⅜ x 20 in. (39.1 x 50.8 cm)
The Estate of David Smith

19
ΔΣ *11-17-51*, 1951
Egg ink, ink and tempera on paper
20 x 26 in. (50.8 x 66 cm)
The Estate of David Smith

20
ΔΣ *10/21/52*, 1952
Egg ink and tempera on paper
15 5/8 x 20 3/4 in. (39.7 x 52.7 cm)
The Estate of David Smith

21
Horizontal 9/4/52, 1952
Steel and brass, on stainless steel base
17 1/2 x 43 3/4 x 7 in. (44.5 x 111.1 x 17.8 cm)
The Estate of David Smith

22
ΔΣ *11/23/51 (Old Snow)*, 1951
Ink on paper
22¾ x 18 in. (57.8 x 45.7 cm)
The Estate of David Smith

23
ΔΣ FEB 2'52, 1952
Egg ink on paper
15 1/2 x 20 1/4 in. (38.1 x 52.1 cm)
The Estate of David Smith

24
Bennington ΔΣ 12-14-52, 1952
Egg ink on paper
42 1/2 x 29 3/4 in. (108 x 75.6 cm)
The Estate of David Smith

25
18 2/54, 1954
Egg ink on paper
8¾ x 11½ in. (22.2 x 29.2 cm)
The Estate of David Smith

26
Untitled, 1954
Ink on paper
8 x 11 in. (20.3 x 27.9 cm)
The Estate of David Smith

27
ΔΣ *14/5/4/53*, 1953
Ink and egg ink on paper
15¾ x 20¼ in. (40 x 51.4 cm)
The Estate of David Smith

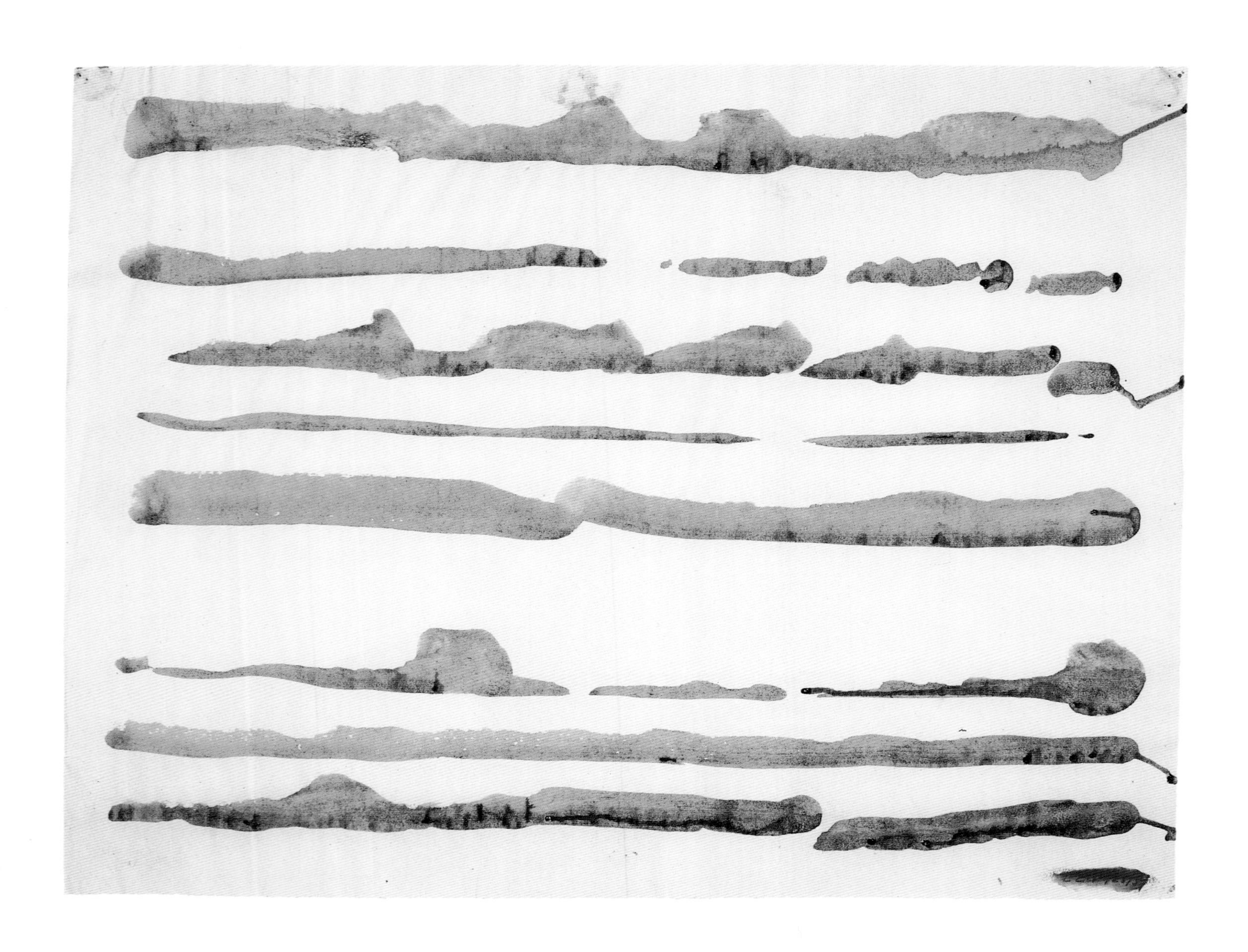

28
ΔΣ 10/23/54, 1954
Egg ink and gouache on paper
19 13/16 x 25 3/4 in. (50.3 x 65.4 cm)
The Estate of David Smith

29
Untitled, 1952
Egg ink and gouache on paper
19⅞ x 25¾ in. (50.5 x 65.4 cm)
The Estate of David Smith

30
ΔΣ *10-9-57*, 1957
Egg ink on paper
15⅝ x 20⅜ in. (39.7 x 51.8 cm)
The Estate of David Smith

31
Untitled, 1954
Egg ink and oil on paper
25½ x 18¾ in. (64.8 x 47.6 cm)
Collection of Tony and Gail Ganz

32
Tower Eight, 1957
Silver
46 ½ x 13 x 10⅝ in. (118.1 x 33 x 27 cm)
Raymond and Patsy Nasher Collection

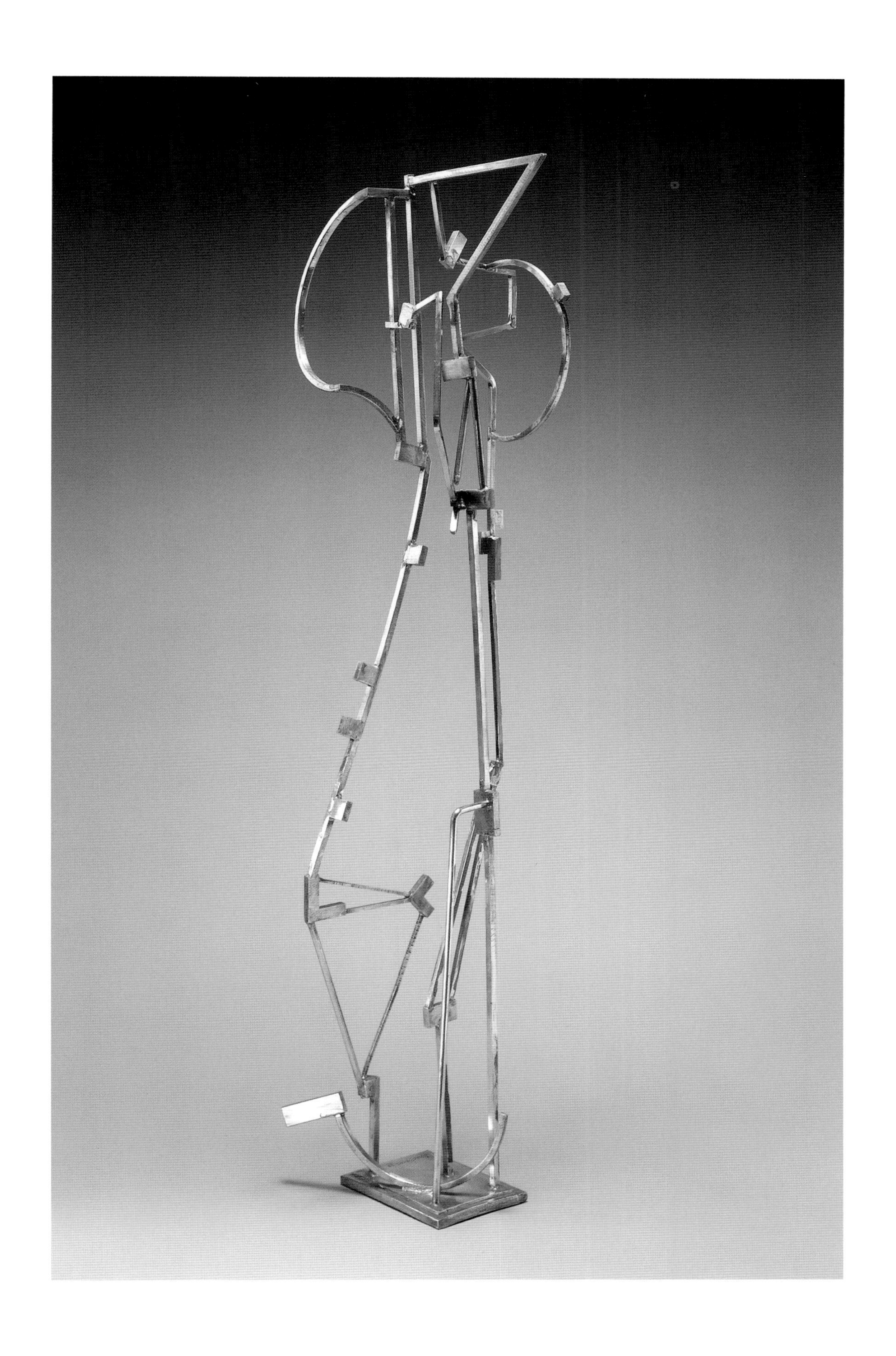

33
ΔΣ 9/4/52 (Study for Tanktotems), 1952
Tempera and ink on paper
18 ¼ x 23⅜ in. (46.4 x 59.4 cm)
The Estate of David Smith

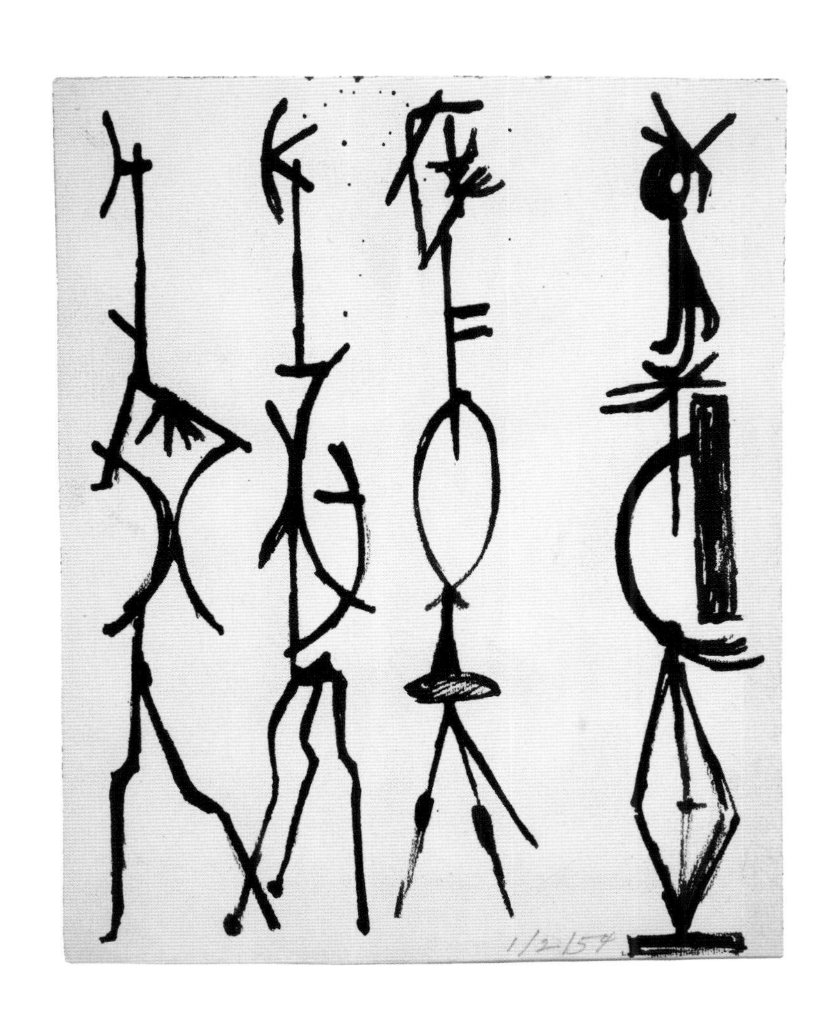

34
Untitled, 1954
Ink on paper
9⅞ x 7⅞ in. (25.1 x 20 cm)
The Estate of David Smith

35
Anchorhead, 1952
Steel, painted
76¾ x 25¾ x 21½ in. (194.9 x 65.4 x 54.6 cm)
The Estate of David Smith

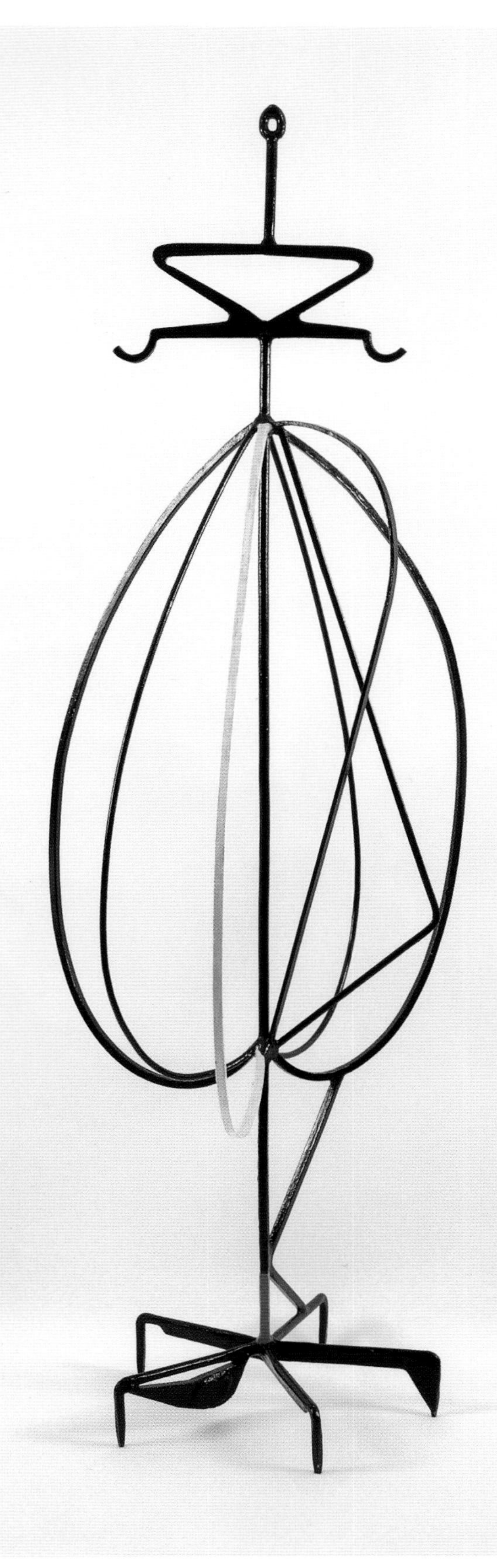

36
Untitled, 1957
Egg ink on paper
18 ⅞ x 26 in. (47.9 x 66 cm)
The Estate of David Smith

37
Untitled (5/3/59), 1959
Egg ink on paper
27⅛ x 39⅞ in. (68.9 x 101.3 cm)
Raymond and Patsy Nasher Collection

38
ΔΣ *10 5/3/53*, 1953
Ink on paper
15½ x 20⅜ in. (39.4 x 51.8 cm)
The Estate of David Smith

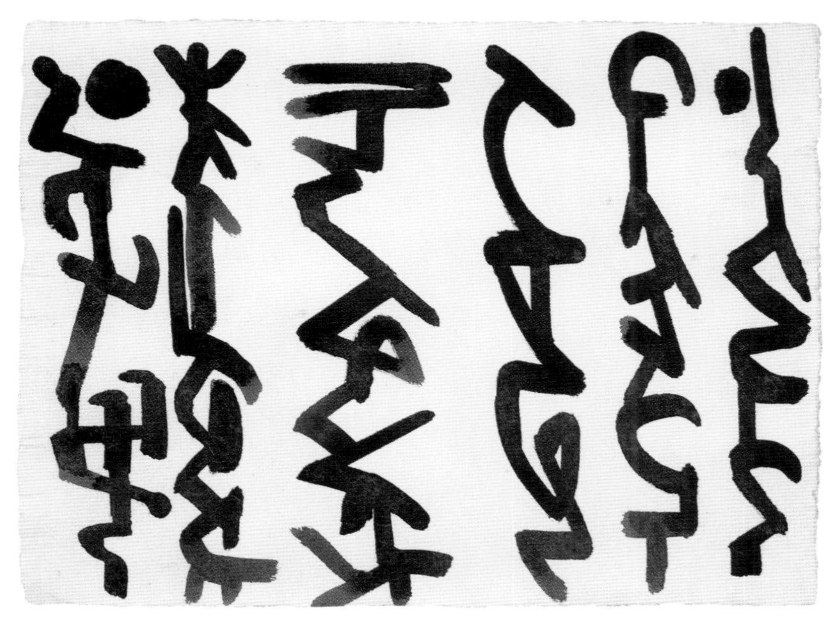

39
Untitled, 1954
Ink on paper
8¾ x 11⅝ in. (22.2 x 29.5 cm)
The Estate of David Smith

40
9 2/54, 1954
Ink on paper
11½ x 8¾ in. (29.2 x 22.2 cm)
The Estate of David Smith

41
Untitled, 1952
Egg ink on paper
22 3/4 x 15 3/4 in. (57.8 x 40 cm)
The Estate of David Smith

42
Untitled, 1962
Spray enamel on paper
17 11/16 x 11 1/2 in. (44.9 x 29.2 cm)
The Estate of David Smith

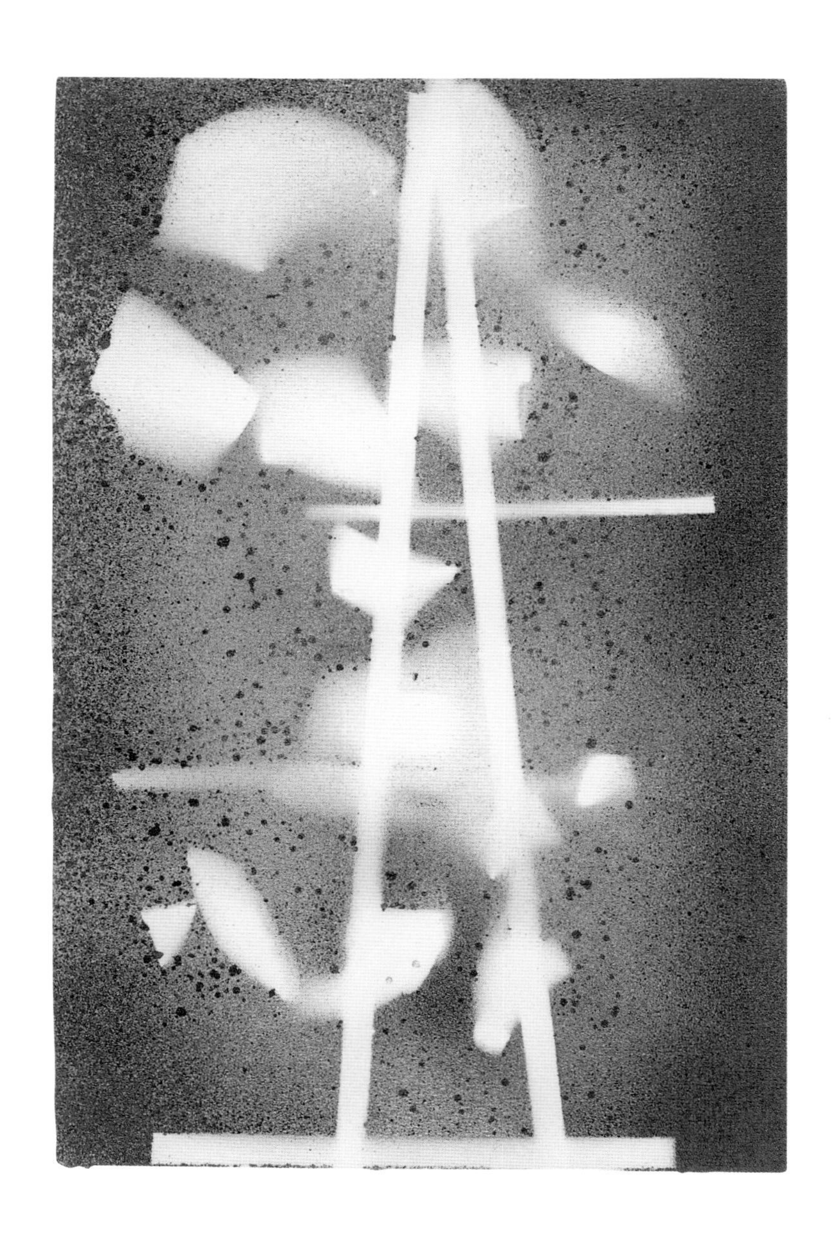

43
Untitled, 1959
Spray enamel on paper
17¾ x 11½ in. (45.1 x 29.2 cm)
The Estate of David Smith

44
Untitled (Three Cubi Studies), 1962–63
Spray enamel on paper
11½ x 16⅜ in. (29.2 x 41.6 cm)
The Estate of David Smith

45
ΔΣ *10/31/54 3*, 1954
Egg ink on paper
17 x 21 in. (43.2 x 53.3 cm)
Collection of Tony and Gail Ganz

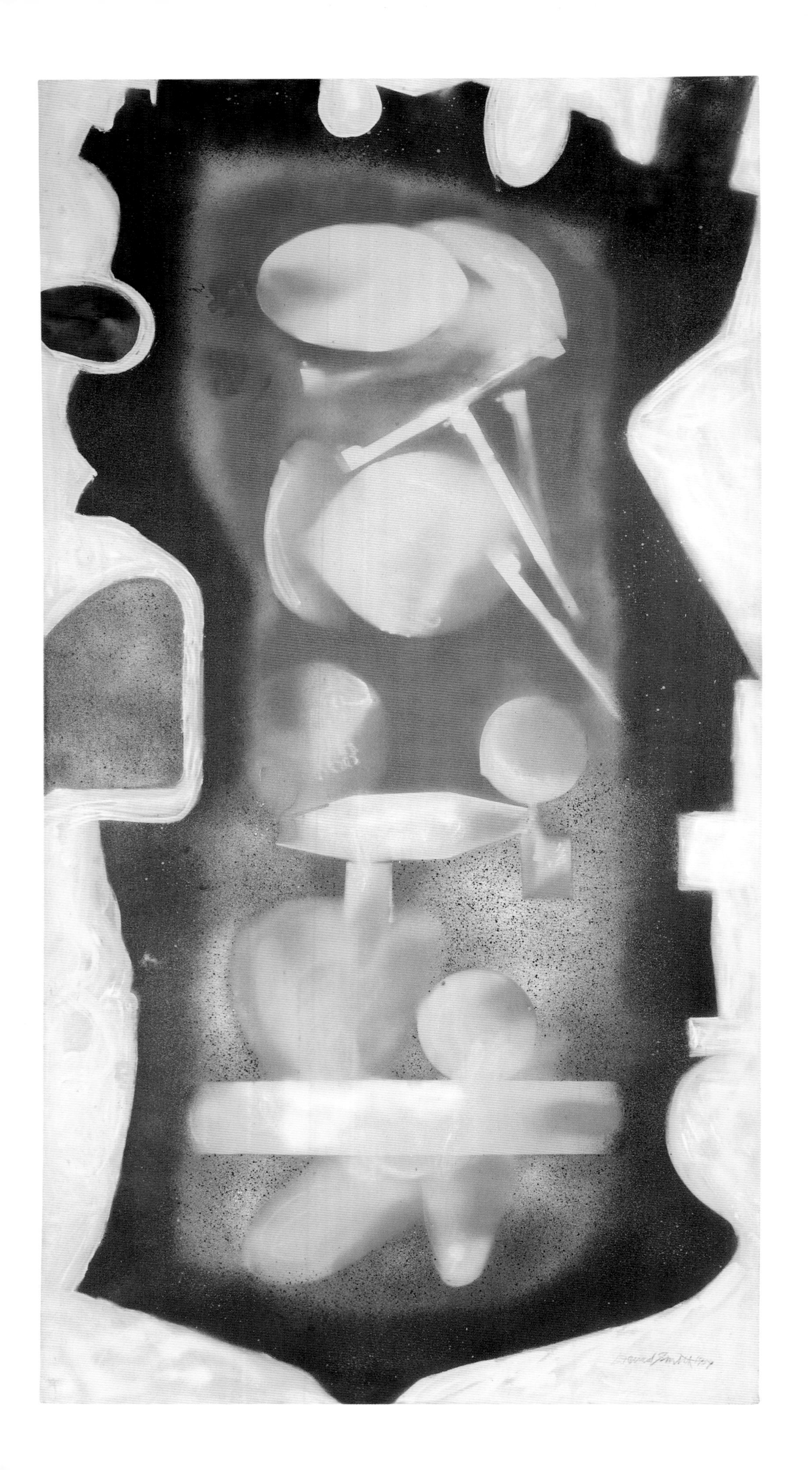

46
Main Prierlot, 1959
Spray enamel on canvas
98 ¼ x 51¾ in. (249.6 x 131.4 cm)
The Estate of David Smith

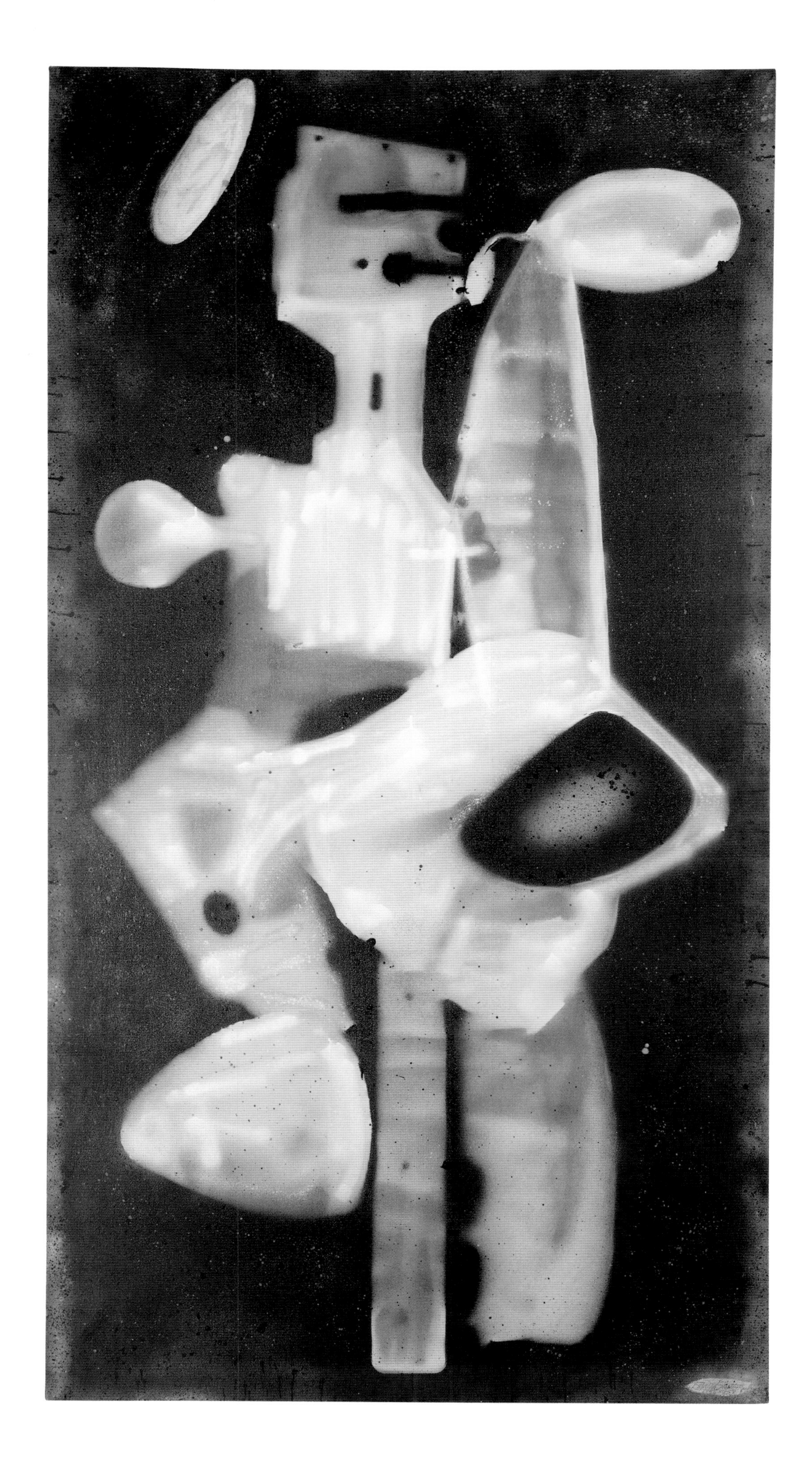

47
Quixote Don, 1958–59
Spray enamel on canvas
98 ¼ x 51½ in. (249.6 x 130.8 cm)
The Estate of David Smith

48
2 Circles on Yellow and Green, 1959
Spray enamel on canvas
106 x 49 in. (269.2 x 124.5 cm)
Raymond and Patsy Nasher Collection

49
Tanktotem IX, 1960
Steel, painted
90 x 33 x 24 1/8 in. (228.6 x 83.8 x 61.3 cm)
The Estate of David Smith

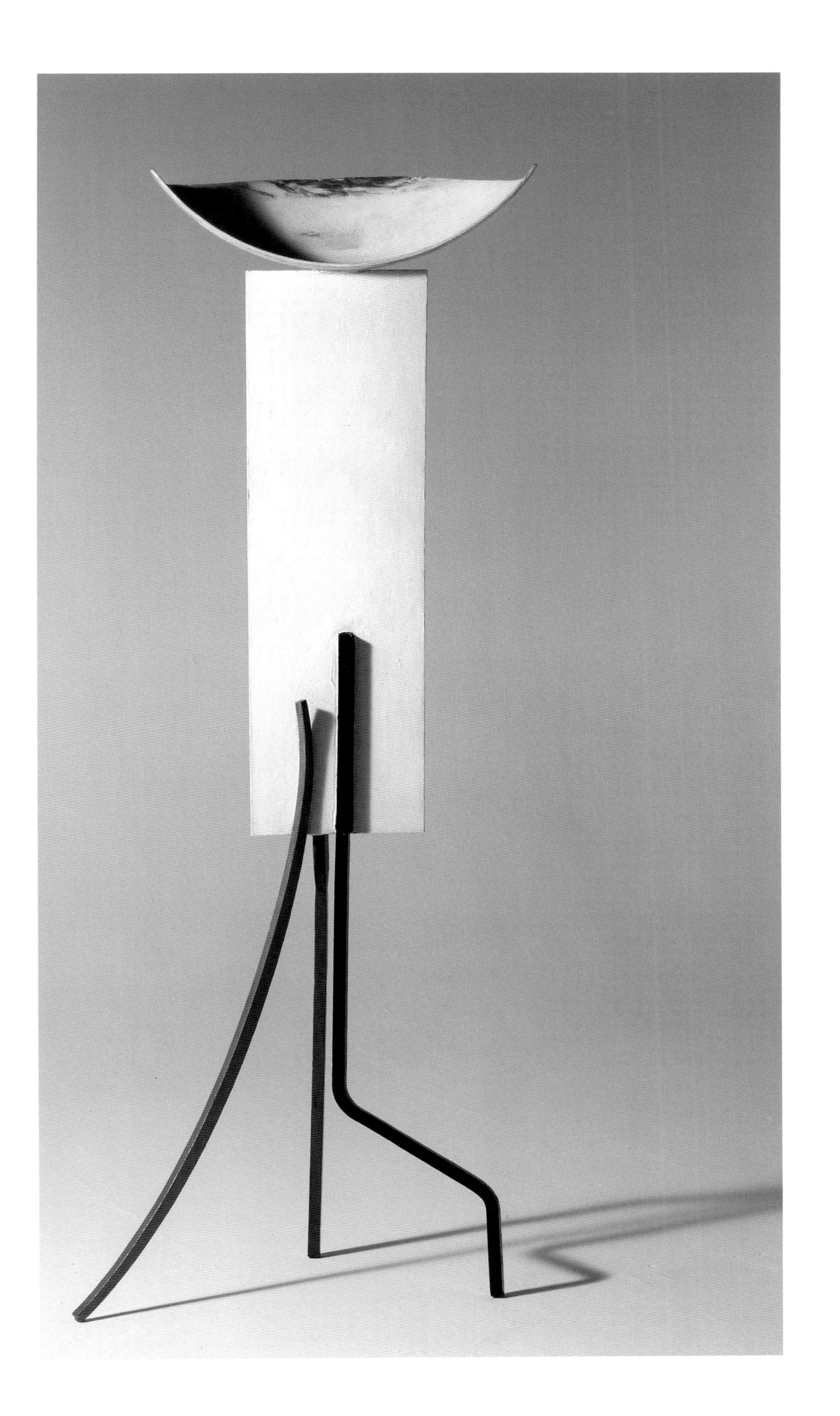

50
Untitled, 1962
Spray enamel on paper
15 5/8 x 20 1/2 in. (39.7 x 52.1 cm)
The Estate of David Smith

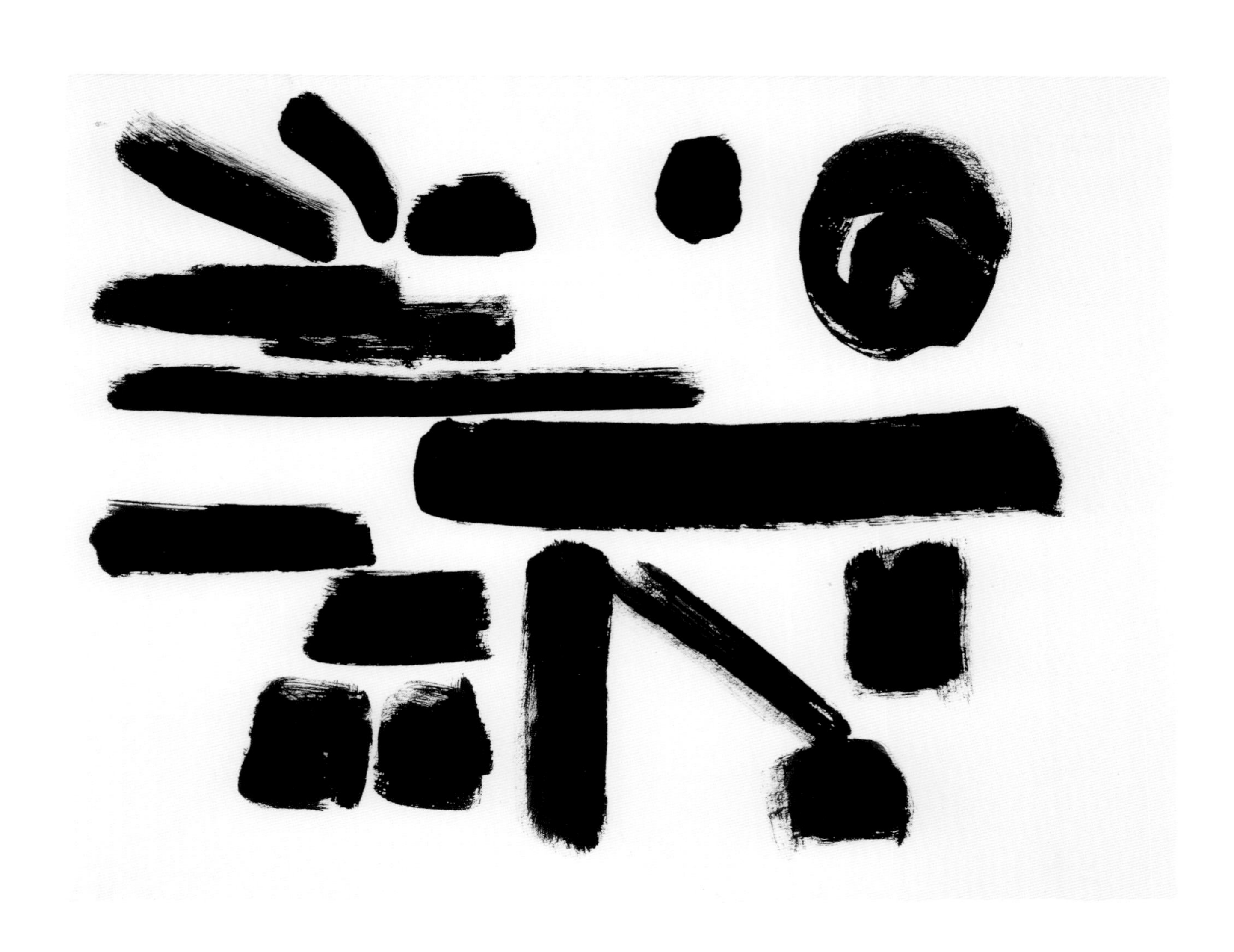

51
XLII, 1960
Egg ink on paper
15⅝ x 20¼ in. (39.7 x 51.4 cm)
The Estate of David Smith

52
Untitled (Nude), 1964
Enamel on canvas
30 x 32 ¼ in. (76.2 x 81.9 cm)
The Estate of David Smith

53
Untitled, 1962
Egg ink on paper
19 x 24 ½ in. (48.3 x 62.2 cm)
The Estate of David Smith

54
Voltri 3, 1962
Egg ink and ink wash on paper
19 x 24½ in. (48.3 x 62.2 cm)
The Estate of David Smith

55
Voltri VI, 1962
Steel
98⅞ x 102¼ x 24 in. (251.1 x 259.7 x 61 cm)
Raymond and Patsy Nasher Collection

56
Untitled, 1962
Spray enamel on paper
13 x 19 in. (33 x 48.3 cm)
The Estate of David Smith

57
Untitled (Voltri) [For Gian Carlo], 1962
Steel
41¼ x 14⅝ x 7⅛ in. (104.8 x 37.1 x 18.1 cm)
Raymond and Patsy Nasher Collection

58
ΔΣ-*Jan 1962*, 1962
Spray enamel on paper
12¾ x 19½ in. (32.4 x 49.5 cm)
The Estate of David Smith

59
Untitled, 1962
Spray enamel on paper
13½ x 19⅞ in. (34.3 x 50.5 cm)
The Estate of David Smith

60
Untitled (Study for Cubi), 1963
Spray enamel on paper
17 ¼ x 12 in. (43.8 x 30.5 cm)
The Estate of David Smith

61
6 ΔΣ 3-16-63, 1963
Spray enamel on paper
17½ x 11½ in. (44.5 x 29.2 cm)
Andrea Woodner, New York

62
Cubi XVII, 1963
Stainless steel
107¾ x 64⅜ x 38⅛ in. (273.7 x 163.5 x 96.8 cm)
Dallas Museum of Art, The Eugene and Margaret McDermott Art Fund, Inc.

63
Voltri XVIII, 1962
Steel
42½ x 34 x 39¾ in. (108 x 86.4 x 101 cm)
Collection of Samuel and Ronnie Heyman, New York

64
Cubi VIII, 1962
Stainless steel
$91\frac{3}{4}$ x 38 x 34 in. (233 x 96.5 x 86.4 cm)
Meadows Museum, Southern Methodist University,
Gift of the Meadows Foundation

65
ΔΣ *3-1-63*, 1963
Spray enamel on paper
16¼ x 11½ in. (41.3 x 29.2 cm)
The Estate of David Smith

66
Untitled, 1957
Oil on canvas
89 x 14 in. (226.1 x 35.6 cm)
The Estate of David Smith

67
Cubi II, 1963
Stainless steel
130½ x 36⅞ x 23⅞ in. (331.5 x 93.7 x 60.6 cm)
The Estate of David Smith

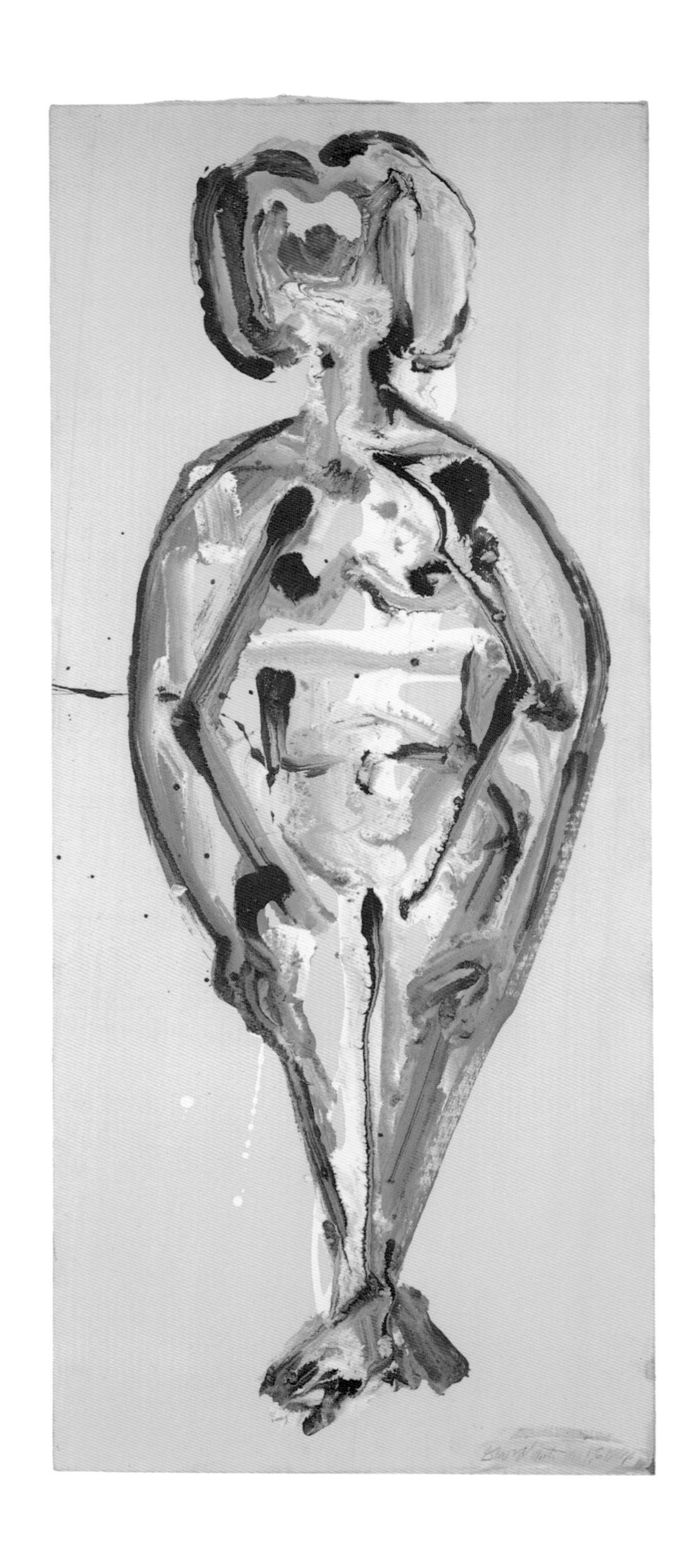

68
Untitled (Nude), 1964
Enamel on canvas
41 x 17½ in. (104.1 x 44.5 cm)
The Estate of David Smith

69
Voltri 4, 1962
Egg ink and gouache on paper
19 x 24½ in. (48.3 x 62.2 cm)
The Estate of David Smith

70
Untitled, 1964
Enamel on canvas
16½ x 59 in. (41.9 x 149.9 cm)
The Estate of David Smith

Statements on Drawing

The following compilation of David Smith's statements on drawing is the most extensive published to date. Although not exhaustive, this collection includes often-quoted phrases that have become canonical in the writing on Smith, as well as many statements that have not appeared in the literature on the artist. Garnett McCoy's invaluable study of Smith's life and writings assembled many of these quotations in 1973. These have been augmented by a review of the microfilm of the David Smith Papers at the Archives of American Art, as well as many of the most informative books, articles, and exhibition catalogues published in the last thirty years.

The artist's recorded statements on drawing span twenty years, from 1945 until just before his death in 1965, at the age of fifty-nine. Taken from personal letters, notes, public speeches, and published interviews, these observations document Smith's intimate engagement with drawing. The subjects range from the mundane to the highly theoretical; from the number of drawings made in a certain period and materials preferred to formal links with sculptures and more poetic musings on the liberating nature of drawing.

Smith's words not only underline the integral role drawing played in his working process, they also reveal the importance he placed on drawing as a foundation for his art and a basic part of his identity. He frequently writes of drawing as an essential conduit of creative ideas, often the quickest and most direct outlet for what, according to Smith, came as an almost unstemmable flow of invention. Additionally, many of the statements depict drawing as a language, direct and honest, whose immediacy of expression constantly revealed the artist's true character or, as Smith sometimes called it, his "secret self."

Correspondence and discussion with critics and fellow artists such as Thomas Hess, David Sylvester, and Jean Xceron allowed Smith to refine and articulate his views on drawing. He also consulted the writings of earlier artists such as Michelangelo Buonarroti, Jean-Auguste-Dominique Ingres, Eugène Delacroix, and Paul Gauguin, copying statements that struck him as particularly meaningful or cogently expressed. These ideas on drawing inform Smith's own statements and place him self-consciously in a lineage of masters who extolled the critical importance of drawing.

Jed Morse

Sources

David Smith Papers, Archives of American Art, Smithsonian Institution, Washington, D.C., with the microfilm reel number followed by the frame number(s). Clark 1985: Trinkett Clark. *The Drawings of David Smith*. Exh. cat. Washington, D.C.: International Exhibitions Foundation, 1985. Gray 1968: Cleve Gray, ed. *David Smith by David Smith*. New York: Holt, Rinehart and Winston, 1968. McCoy 1973: Garnett McCoy, ed. *David Smith*. New York: Praeger Publishers, 1973.

I am bound by a personal outlook, which for me gets solved by work—which I fight to do. I have a dilatory tendency—there is so much to be read—so many women to lay—so much liquor to drink—fish to catch, etc.—but I get the most satisfaction out of my work but I got to have enough of "that there"—the more I work the more it flows (the concept). Sometimes while I'm working on one piece I get a conception for a wholly new and different one—on the last two pieces—I've quickly drawn a new one, different, but suggested in a thought process somehow which took place during the manual work on the other. I would say that my product is always about a year's work behind my conceptions, in number. Right now I have drawings and thinkings for a year's labor.

From a letter to Edgar Levy, September 1, 1945. Archives, ND-Smith, unfilmed papers, Box 20. See also McCoy 1973, p. 196; Clark 1985, p. 26.

Ingres told young Degas, "Draw lines, young man, many lines—from memory or from nature—it is in this way that you will become a good artist."

A handwritten note in notebook 27, late 1940s. Archives, ND-Smith 3/1011.

You talk about preconceived pictures. I say sometimes yes—to a degree—and sometimes no. Sculpture is a little different. Only occasionally can I start out with no preconceived subject or point. I usually have a drawing for the start. Painting is more fluid, and you can make a lot of approaches towards a solution within or on the same canvas plane, but sculpt[ing] isn't as flexible. I haven't found a rule for myself on the approach. The end product is the thing. I get nearer each time, but that vision—can still see farther away.

From a letter to Edgar Levy, April 24, 1948. McCoy 1973, p. 20.

Note especially the lyrical quotes as chapter heads, such as the Goethe conversation to Blaze de Bury, which starts "We talk too much, we should talk less and draw more, etc." (This should be our studio motto...).

From Smith's comments on books he assigned to his class, May 2, 1950. Archives, ND-Smith 4/521–522.

To the serious students I would not teach the analysis of art or art history—I would first teach drawing; teach the student to become so fluent that drawing becomes the language to replace words. Art is made without words. It doesn't need words to explain it or encourage its making.... I make no separate provision for the cause of sculpture apart from painting. The preference governing actual material is personal. The concept in either art comes from the expression of emotion and thought. The difference in technical pursuit does not change the mind's reaction to form.... In my own case I don't know whether I make some pieces as painted sculpture or paintings in form.

"What I Believe About the Teaching of Sculpture," lecture given at a panel on the Teaching of Sculpture, Midwestern University Art Conference, Louisville, Kentucky, October 27, 1950. McCoy 1973, p. 63–64.

I have hundreds of sculptures on paper which time and conceptual change have passed by.

From sketchbooks and notebooks no. 40, 1950–54. Archives, ND-Smith 3/1339. See also Clark 1985, p. 25.

I follow no set procedure in starting a sculpture. Some works start out as chalk drawings on the cement floor, with cut steel forms working into the drawings. When the structure can become united, it is welded into position upright. Then the added dimension requires different considerations over the more or less profile form of the floor drawing assembly.

Sometimes I make a lot of drawings using possibly one relationship on each drawing which will add up in the final work. Sometimes sculptures just start with no drawing at all.... My drawings are made either in work books or on large sheets of linen rag. I stock bundles of several types, forgetting the cost so I can be free with it. The cost problem I have to forget on everything, because it is always more than I can afford—more than I get back from sales—most years, more than I earn.

Notes for "David Smith Makes a Sculpture," an article by Elaine de Kooning, *Art News*, September 1951. The notes were reprinted intact in *Art News*, January 1969. Archives, ND-Smith 4/490. See also McCoy 1973, p. 73.

Certain Japanese formalities seem close to me, such as the beginning of a stroke outside the paper continuing through the drawing space to project beyond, so that the included part possesses both the power of origin and projection. This produces the impression of strength, and if drops fall, they become attributes or relationships. Similarly, if the brush flows dry into hair marks, such may be greater in energy, having at least a natural quality not to be reworked, being sufficient in intent to convey the stronger content. It is not Japanese painting but some of the principles involved that have meaning to me. Another Japanese concept demands that when representing an object suggesting strength—like rocks, talons, claws, tree branches—the moment the brush is applied the sentiment of strength must be invoked and felt through the artist's system, and so transmitted into the object painted. And that this nervous current must be continuous and of equal intensity while the work proceeds. As my material already possesses strength akin to the Japanese power-stroke intent, I take delight in using steel as a fluid with which to fashion velvet form within images when the intensity and feeling are the forces within the concept.

From a draft of "The New Sculpture," a paper presented at the symposium "The New Sculpture," The Museum of Modern Art, New York, February 1, 1952. Archives, ND-Smith 4/358–59. Final version reprinted in McCoy 1973, pp. 82–85.

For instance, the sculpture called *Hudson River Landscape* came in part from drawings made on a train between Albany and Poughkeepsie. A synthesis of drawings from ten trips over a seventy-five mile stretch; yet later when I shook a quart bottle of India ink it flew over my hand, it looked like my landscape. I placed my hand on paper—from the image left I traveled with the landscape to other landscapes and their objects—with additions, deductions, directives which flashed past too fast to tabulate but elements of which are in the sculpture. Is *Hudson River Landscape* the Hudson River or is it the travel, the vision; or does it matter? The sculpture exists on its own, it is an entity. The name is an affectionate designation of the point prior to the travel. My object was not these words or the Hudson River but the existence of the sculpture. Your response may not travel down the Hudson River, but it may travel on any river or on a higher level, travel through form-response by choice known better by your own recall. I have intensified only part of the related clues; the sculpture possesses nothing unknown to you. I want you to travel, by perception, the path I traveled in creating it.

From "The Language is Image," *Arts and Architecture* 69 (February 1952), pp. 20–21, 33–34. See also McCoy 1973, p. 81.

I rarely work with a preconceived conviction about the end of a sculpture. I rarely work from a drawing. The sculpture starts with a directive since I need the physical labor to be balanced with the mental and conceptual battle. I make 300 to 400 large drawings a year, usually with egg yolk and Chinese ink and brushes. These drawings are studies for sculpture, sometimes what sculpture is, sometimes what sculpture can never be. Sometimes they are atmospheres from which sculptural form is unconsciously selected during the labor process of producing form. Then again they may be amorphous floating direct statements in which I am the subject, and the drawing is the act. They are all statements of my identity and come from the constant work stream. I title these drawings with the numerical noting of month day and year. I never intend a day to pass without asserting my identity, my work records my existence.

My sculpture and especially my drawings relate to my past works, the 3 or 4 works in progress and to the visionary projection of what the next sculptures are to be. One of these projections is to push beauty to the very edge of rawness. To push beauty and imagination farther towards the limit of accepted state, to keep it moving, and to keep the edge moving, to shove it as far as possible towards that precious edge where beauty balances but does not topple over the edge of the vulgar.

From a draft of a lecture given in Portland, Oregon, on March 23, 1953. Archives, ND-Smith 4/387–88. See also Gray 1968, p. 104; Clark. 1985, pp. 16, 29.

21. Why do you hesitate—why can you not draw objects as freely as you can write their names and speak words about them?
22. What has caused this mental block? If you can name, dream, recall vision and auras why can't you draw them? In the conscious act of drawing, who is acting in your unconscious as censor?

...In particular to the painter—
Is there as much art in a drawing as in a watercolor—or as in an oil painting?
Do you think drawing is a complete and valid approach to art vision, or a preliminary only toward a more noble product?
In particular to the sculptor—

If a drawing is traced, even with the greatest precision, from another drawing, you will perceive that the one is a copy. Although the differences may deviate less than half a hair, recognizable only by perceptual sensitivity, unanimously we rule the work of the intruder's hand as non-art.

But where is the line of true art—when the sculptor's process often introduces the hands of a plaster caster, the mold maker, the grinder and the polisher, and the patina applier, all these processes and foreign hands intruding deviations upon what was once the original work?

From a series of questions in an undated typescript among the David Smith Papers. McCoy dates this ca. 1953–54. McCoy 1973, pp. 112–13.

To make a mark—to set a stroke—which demands its space, to defile the white sheet or make the mark of honor, to erect a solid or set a limitation, how many voices defy you, are ready to tear it down because it has no words? Are the voices to be or old memory echoes? Are these the strokes which elicit sympathy, or are these the strokes that isolate the differences? Who are you making them for—you and whom else? Are all essential, or is essential ideal and inhuman—a vanity, a ballet of poses needing words for music to give it the illusion of unity? That stroke, is it a figure—is it I there in space, an ancestor, or am I outside looking into the mirror? And is it noble like a sumi stroke, or is it weak in spots like I? Or do I brag, or aspire, or am I distant enough to be impartial? Or does it yield to others, that it is not all mine or me? And am I solo or are we in unison—or should I be embarrassed or is it all in the day's work? Whatever, it does not deal death—I need not have guilt like a scientist. Nor does it exploit the day labor for profit—nor sell a product. Has it been led to trap by a name? Have words baited what should be vision? And if you name it, is it too worn?

From a series of handwritten notes, ca. 1955.[1] Archives, ND-Smith 4/956–57, Writings and notes, undated.

1 These words appear on a portion of microfilm reel 4 dedicated to undated papers; however, Smith wrote them on the letterhead of University of Mississippi, where he taught in 1955. Written as a stream of undifferentiated thoughts, I have added punctuation for clarity.

"The science of drawing or of line, if you wish to call it that, is the source and the very essence of drawing, of sculpture, of architecture and of every kind of representation as well as the root of all the sciences. He who rises to the point where he can master it possesses a great treasure."

—Michelangelo [Buonarroti]

"Drawings are the first ideas of a painter, the first flash of his imagination, his style, his spirit, his way of thinking.... A painter while painting corrects himself and restrains the impulses of his genius; while making a drawing he dashes off the first flash of his thought; he yields to himself; he shows himself as he is. A painter's way of drawing is as distinctive as handwriting and much more revealing than a writer's style."

—[Antoine-Joseph] Dezallier d'Argenville

"With great artists the sketch is not a fantasy, a confused cloud; it is something else than a collection of scarcely perceptible tracings. Only the great artists start from a fixed point, and that is that pure expression to which it is so difficult for them to return in the long and rapid execution of their work."

—[Eugène] Delacroix

"Have you ever noticed that when you re-copy a sketch that you are pleased with, and which was done in the moment or second of inspiration, all you get is an inferior copy, especially if you correct the proportions and the mistakes that reason thinks it finds there?"

—[Paul] Gauguin

"The most spontaneous expression of artistic understanding is found in sketches. They express what is essential for the artist and through them one may observe how he thinks."

—[Heinrich] Woelfflin
From a typed list of "Statements on drawing" Smith collected in 1955.[2]
ND-Smith 4/970–72, Writings and notes, undated.

Many students think of drawing as something hasty and preparatory before painting or making a sculpture. A sort of purgatory between amateurism and accomplishment. As a preliminary before the great act, because everybody can draw some, and children are uninhibited about it and do it so easily, and writing itself is a style of drawing, and it is common on sidewalks, board fences, phone booths, etc.

But actually only a very experienced artist may appreciate the challenge, because it is so common an expression. It is also the most revealing, having no high expectancy to maintain, not even the authenticating quality of gold frames to artificially price or lend grandeur to its atmosphere. And, by its very conditioning, it comes much closer to the actual bareness of the soul and the nature of free expressionism.

It is not expected to carry the flourish, the professionalism of oil painting, nor the accuracy and mannered clarity in the formal brushing of the watercolorist.

If it is pompous, artificial, pretentious, insincere, mannered, it is so evident, so quick to be detected, and like the written line, it is a quickly recognized key to personality. If it is timid, weak, overbold, or blustering, it is revealed much as one perceives it in the letter or a signature. There is not the demand or tradition for technique and conformity. The pureness of statement, the honesty of expression, is laid bare in a black-and-white answer of who that mark-maker is, what he stands for, how strong his conviction is, or how weak. Often his true personality is revealed before repetitions or safer symbols can come to his defense. More his truth than other media with technique and tradition, more his truth than words can express, more free from thinking in words than polished techniques, drawing is more shaped like he is shaped, because the pressure of performance has not made him something he isn't.

The drawing that comes from the serious hand can be unwieldy, uneducated, unstyled and still be great simply by the superextension of whatever conviction the artist's hand projects and being so strong that it eclipses the standard qualities critically expected. The need, the drive to express

2 This list appears on a portion of microfilm reel 4 dedicated to undated writings and notes. However, at the top of the first page appears the handwritten note "Statements on drawing, Sculpture 1955." The end of the list bears another handwritten note identifying the translator of these statements as "Prof. Bowie of our Art library," most likely at the University of Mississippi, where Smith taught in 1955.

can be so strong that the drawing makes its own reason for being.

Drawing is the most direct, closest to the true self, the most natural liberation of man—and if I may guess back to the action of very early man, it may have been the first celebration of man with his secret self—even before song.

But its need doesn't stand on primitive reconstruction—anyone knows, everyone feels the need to draw. I truly believe that anything anyone has seen he can draw, and that everyone here has now seen everything he ever will see, and that all that stands between his drawing anything in the world is his own inhibition. What that is we don't know. Each must dig himself out of his own mind and liberate the act of drawing to the vision of memory. It is not so much that this correlation is impossible—but more the mental block that keeps him from trying that which he deems impossible.

We are blocked from creative ways of expressing by ways we feel about things and by ways we think we ought to feel, by word pictures that cancel out creative vision, and intimidations that limit creative expression.

If drawing could come now as easily as when a man was six, he would not doubt or think, he would do. But since he approaches it more consciously and not with a child's freedom, he must admit to himself that he is making a drawing—and he approaches mark-making humbly, self-consciously, or timidly. Here he finds pressure and intimidation and inhibition. But the first mark of drawing is made. Sometimes it takes courage to make this one statement. This stroke is as good as he can make, now. The next and those to come lead toward creative freedom. He must try to be himself in the stroke. He dominates the line related to image and does not permit the image to dominate him and the line. Not a line the way others think the line should be—not how history says it once was; nor what multitudes say they cannot do with a straight line. For a line so drawn with conviction is straighter in context than the ruler.

The deviations outside mechanical realism, which, usually with a bit of hostility, represent the average expectancy, are the nature of human line—the inaccuracies, so-called, are often other images trying to assert themselves in association. And the truth of image is not single, it is many—the image in memory is many actions and many things—often trying to express its subtle overlapping in only one line or shape.

Simply stated, the line is a personal-choice line. The first stroke demands another in complement, the second may demand a third in opposition, and the approach continues, each stroke more free because confidence is built by effort. If the interest in this line gesture making is sustained, and the freedom of the act developed, realization to almost any answer can be attained. Soon confidence is developed and one of the secrets of drawing felt, and marks come so easily and move so fast that no time is left to think.

Even the drawing made before the performance is often greater, more truthful, more sincere than the formal production later made from it. Such a statement will find more agreement with artists than from connoisseurs. Drawings are usually not pompous enough to be called works of art. They are often too truthful. Their appreciation neglected, drawings remain the life force of the artist.

Especially is this true for the sculptor, who, of necessity, works in media slow to take realization. And where the original creative impetus must be maintained during labor, drawing is the fast-moving search which keeps physical labor in balance.

A lecture given at a forum conducted by George Rickey at Sophie Newcomb College, Tulane University, New Orleans, March 21, 1955. A draft of the speech can be found in the Archives, ND-Smith 4/451–53. Final version reprinted in McCoy 1973, pp. 119–20, 137.

Remember May 1935, when we walked down 57 St. after your show at Garland Gallery, how you influenced me to concentrate on sculpture? I'm of course forever glad that you did, it's more my energy, though I make two hundred color drawings a year and sometimes painting, but by having my identity as a sculptor, I can paint and I thus know myself better. But I paint or draw as a sculptor, I have no split identity as I did in 1935. Forever thanks.

From a letter to Jean Xceron, February 7, 1956. McCoy 1973, p. 206.

...There are a lot of things I wish people had taught me. I wish somebody had taught me to draw in proportion to my own size, to draw as freely and as easily, with the same movements that I dressed myself with, or that I ate with, or worked with in the factory. Instead I was required to use a little brush, a little pencil, to work on a little area, which put me into a position of knitting—not exactly my forte. There wasn't a movement in my life up until that time that ever made me knit or make a tile design. I think that the first thing that I should have been taught was to work on great big paper, big sizes to utilize my natural movements toward what we will call art. It doesn't matter what it might look like. I think the freedom of gesture and courage to act are more important than trying to make a design.

... When a student fails to do his assignment and gives an excuse instead, after two excuses I just assign a hundred extra drawings—that's a new requirement of the course for them before they can pass. That's not so bad. I've seen dullards, after they did a hundred drawings under pressure, get so they liked to draw. One of the best students I had was a girl to whom I once gave this assignment. Of course, we may have had to decide what was a drawing. I accepted the definition of drawing as any piece of paper that had a mark on it, on the basis of self-respect. A student wouldn't give you a hundred pieces of paper with a mark on each one. Possibly one sheet of paper with one mark, but it isn't long before he feels the need of more than one mark. By the time students make three or four marks they are already draftsmen. Everybody is intimidated about marks on paper, or marks on canvas. One is a very simple thing to do. You must help to uninhibit or unintimidate people before they can get involved in the creative act. I think that is one of the important things in teaching—to unintimidate. Freedom should be first before judgement and self-criticism.

Utilizing another atmosphere is often an elevating aid in drawing. Music appeals to me in that way, rather than art history or art appreciation. I would much rather teach with music.

From "Memories to Myself," a speech given at the Eighteenth Conference of the National Committee on Art Education, The Museum of Modern Art, New York, May 5, 1960.
McCoy 1973, pp. 149, 152.

DAVID SMITH: I painted for some years. I've never given it up; I always, even if I'm having trouble with a sculpture, I always paint my troubles out.

...

DAVID SYLVESTER: Have you ever had any temptation to work in traditional materials, carving or modeling?

DSM: I do both. I model in wax and make bronzes that way, and I carve sometimes; some of my early work was carved. I don't choose to close out any method, approach, or material. Oh, I draw. I draw figures and things like that at times.

DSY: Do you ever do it from a model? Do you ever do it from nature?

DSM: Sure. As a matter of study and a matter of balance. I draw a great deal, because sculpture is such hard work and if I put in ten or eleven hours a day or more at hard labor, you know, the sort of dirty work of my profession, I like to take a bath and change my clothes and spend the rest of the day drawing.

...

DSY: And this, of course, connects you very closely with the painters of your generation, doesn't it? I mean this to-and-fro between the artist and the material, this special emphasis on it now. This makes you very closely linked with Pollock and de Kooning.

DSM: Well, we were all friends and I talked with painters and I belong with painters, in a sense; and all of my early friends were painters because we all studied together. And I never conceived of myself as anything other than a painter because my work came right through the raised surface and color and objects applied to the surface. Some of the greatest contributions of sculpture to the twentieth century are by painters. Had it not been for painters, sculpture would be in a very sorry position.

Some of the greatest departures in the concept of sculpture have been made by Picasso and Matisse. There was a series of heads that Matisse made called... *Jeanette*; in there are some of the very brilliant departures in the concept of sculpture. Painting and sculpture aren't very far apart.

Excerpts from an interview with David Sylvester, New York, June 16, 1961, published in *Living Arts*, April 1964. See also Gray 1968, p. 106; McCoy 1973, pp. 172–74.

DAVID SMITH: I'm a sensualist... but I don't use a sketch when I make sculpture, ordinarily.
THOMAS HESS: You make chalk drawings on the floor.
DS: Oh, that's when I'm in trouble.
TH: What do you mean, "no sketches?" You're always drawing.
DS: Well, I don't make drawings seldom. I do what I need to do, Tom, and sometimes I think I'm stronger and there are more possibilities open for invention if I don't use the sketch. I draw a lot to increase my mind or my vision, but when I work, I try to let the work make its own vision—while I keep a history of knowing behind it.

...

TH: What about the Wagons?
DS: I've got three on wheels. It's a kind of iron chariot, on four wheels, with open linear elements. Each section of drawing is totally unrelated, and they don't fall together. They just sit there, broken.
TH: So the chariot becomes a kind of field where these things exist?
DS: A longitudinal field.

...

TH: In the longitudinal space are "drawings"?
DS: Big forgings. I drew a number of forgings to order, about forty-five, and sent them to Pittsburgh to be made.
TH: In steel?
DS: Steel, yes.

...

TH: ...I remember a piece, fifteen years ago, with a pedestal, steel, then a plane divided into three sections and in each section there were series of shapes and, above that, some steel drawing.
DS: That was a letter... and that relates to the Little Red Hen that scratched in Joyce...
The Little Red Hen that scratched the letter up.
TH: A steel letter.
DS: Yes. And the letter says "You sent for me." Something very simple. A short cryptic message. "You sent for me." All letters say, "You sent for me," as far as I'm concerned.

...

TH: And you've done some big linear sculptures which aren't "letters"—*Australia*...
DS: Yes, and *Hudson River Landscape*; it was a matter of drawing.
TH: You think of drawing in terms of writing?
DS: I don't differentiate between writing and drawing, not since I read that part of Joyce.
TH: There is a kind of secret message?
DS: The little hen scratched up a secret message.
TH: "I sent for you?"
DS: No. "You sent for me"—that's different. That's what I think the secret letter said. Nobody knows what the letter really said.

Excerpts from "The Secret Letter," an interview with Thomas B. Hess, June 1964, published in October of the same year in the catalog of the David Smith exhibition at Marlborough-Gerson Gallery, New York. See also McCoy 1973, pp. 181, 184–86.

That's a sculpture about seven or eight or nine feet high, and it is just one single bar forged; but I don't think I could ever make a sculpture like that without making three hundred or four hundred drawings a year—I think it has to develop that way. If you are interested in making a vertical, simple vertical with the development of a drawing concept. I was wondering about a line, you see; here's the center part of it, and this form in here.... And it is a drawing line really. I would never have done that if I hadn't been interested in drawing lines. I think that is about nine feet high, and a very skinny one.

From a lecture given at Bennington College, Bennington, Vermont, May 12, 1965
Clark 1985, p. 30.

Some critics refer to certain pieces of my sculpture as "two-dimensional." Others call it "line drawing." I do not admit to this, either conceptually or physically. It may be true in part, but only as one attribute of many, and that by intention and purpose. There are no rules in sculpture. This particular criticism is not sufficient or valid grounds for dismissal.

I make no apologies for my end-views. They are as important as they are intended to be. If a sculpture could be a line drawing, then speculate that a line drawing removed from its paper bond and viewed from the side would be a beautiful thing, one which I would delight in seeing in the work of other artists. The end-view or profile of an interesting person or object arouses the mind to contemplation of the imagined personality and physiognomy, since a work of art or object of interest is always completed by the viewer and is never seen the same by any two persons.

From a draft of an undated speech.
ND-Smith 4/823, Writings and notes, undated.
See also Gray 1968, p. 68.

As Odilon Redon expressed it, the more ambitious study doesn't give as enduring results as those fragmentary passages that come without thought of composition. It is not the ambitious study which the artist will consult when he needs help. The naïve study—when one forgets what one knows and approaches what one sees with humility—remains a document, fruitful, inexhaustible in its lessons, and one that will never tire.

From a handwritten note in an undated notebook.
Archives, ND-Smith 4/883, Writings and notes, undated.

Biography

1906–25
Born March 9 in Decatur, Indiana. Father, Harvey Martin Smith, was a telephone engineer and part-time inventor. Mother, Golda Stoler Smith, was a schoolteacher. 1921, moves with family to Paulding, Ohio. While still in high school, enrolls in a correspondence course in cartooning from Cleveland Art School. Studies for one year at Ohio University, Athens, and briefly at Notre Dame University. Works for the Studebaker automobile factory (South Bend, Indiana) as a riveter; also does soldering, spot-welding and works a lathe. Takes a job in Studebaker's Finance Agency (until 1927).

1926–28
Moves to Washington, D.C., then to New York to work at the Morris Plan Bank. Meets a young painter, Dorothy Dehner (they marry in 1927), who is studying at the Art Student's League (ASL). Smith enrolls at the ASL, taking evening painting classes with Richard Lahey. Fall 1927 until 1931, studies full time at the ASL. Takes classes with the American realist painter John Sloan, drawing instructor Kimon Nicolaides, and Czech modernist painter Jan Matulka, a former pupil of Hans Hoffman. After Matulka's classes at ASL end in 1928, Smith studies with him privately (to 1931). Matulka introduces Smith to the works of Mondrian, Picasso, Kandinsky, and the Russian Constructivists. Smith also explores other aspects of New York's cultural life, developing strong interests in jazz and modern dance that will continue through his life.

February–May 1928, Smith works for the A.G. Spalding sporting goods store. May, leaves to be a seaman on an oil tanker, sailing from Philadelphia through Panama, to San Pedro, California. Fall, returns to New York. Works at Spalding (until October 1931) while living with Dehner in Brooklyn.

1929–30
Summer, Smith and Dehner visit Bolton Landing, near Lake George in the Adirondack Mountains in upstate New York, where they buy a dilapidated house and barn on seventy-seven acres of land. For the next eleven years (until 1940) they go upstate every summer and fall.

Meets John Graham, Polish émigré, intellectual and artist. Through Graham, meets avant-garde painters Stuart Davis, Jean Xceron, Arshile Gorky, and Willem de Kooning. Sees Picasso's 1928 *Project for Sculpture* in 1929 issue of *Cahiers d'Art*. Experiments with painting, collage, and reliefs created in an abstract Surrealist style. Becomes increasingly interested in combining construction and painting.

1931–33
Smith and Dehner travel to St. Thomas, Virgin Islands (October 1931–June 1932). Smith paints, assembles small constructions using pieces of wood, coral and other found objects, casts first stone sculpture, and experiments with photography.

Summer 1932, installs a forge and an anvil in Bolton Landing studio. Makes more constructions from wood, wire, stone, aluminum rod, soldered metal, and "found" materials. Begins to weld metal sculptures using oxyacetylene torch.

1934–36
Smith rents working space in a shed on the Brooklyn waterfront that houses "Terminal Iron Works, Boiler-Tube Makers and Ship-Deck." This is his main studio until 1940. Throughout the 1930s, works in the mural and public sculpture departments of various U.S. government-sponsored public works art programs.

John Graham gives Smith a Julio González sculpture, *Head* (c.1927). October 1935, travels for the first time to Europe, with Dehner. After a month in Paris, they visit Athens, Crete, Naples, Malta, Marseilles and London, then travel by steamer ship to Leningrad and Moscow for a twenty-one day tour. Sees the great collection at the Museum of Modern Western Art in Moscow including works by Matisse, Cézanne, and Picasso. (The collection was later divided between the Pushkin Museum of Fine Arts in Moscow and The State Hermitage Museum in Leningrad, now St. Petersburg). July 4, 1936, returns to New York.

1937
Joins the newly organized American Abstract Artists group (while also a member of a variety of other artistic groups) and exhibits with them in 1938 and 1939. Affected by the rise of fascism and German war medals he had seen in Europe, Smith begins work on a series of fifteen bronze medallions he calls *Medals for Dishonor* (finished and exhibited in 1940).

1938–39
January, first one-man show (welded iron sculptures and drawings, 1935–38) opens at Marian Willard's East River Gallery, in New York City. Makes his first arc-welded sculptures. Exhibits sculpture in a group show, *American Art Today*, at the 1938 New York World's Fair.

1940–41
February, speaks in favor of abstract art as against the then fashionable Social Realism in first recorded lecture, "On Abstract Art in America," presented at a forum of the United American Artists group. March, one-man show at Neumann/Willard Gallery, New York. Positive review by Clement Greenberg in *The Nation*.

Spring 1940, Smith and Dehner move permanently to Bolton Landing, taking the name Terminal Iron Works for his studio. Works as a machinist in nearby Glens Falls. During the War years, Smith makes and sells relatively few sculptures. Steel and iron are scarce; works with other materials including marble, cast aluminum, and wood. Continues to draw and paint. Themes range from the violence of war and rape to music and dance as symbols of creativity.

1942–49
At Bolton Landing, Smith brings in electricity and builds a cinderblock, open plan machine-shop studio with a concrete floor. Lives in Schenectady, New York, (near Albany) and works the midnight to 8 a.m. shift, 6 days a week, for the American Locomotive Company, assembling M7 destroyer tanks and locomotives. After getting off work, often drives forty miles to Saratoga, where he learns to work with marble while employed half-days at Saratoga Funeral Monument Yard. January 1942, included in a group show, *American Sculpture of Our Time*, at Willard and Buchholz Galleries, New York. Clement Greenberg writes in *The Nation* about Smith's *Interior* (1937): "If [Smith] is able to maintain the level set in the work he has already done, he has a chance of becoming the greatest of all American Artists." April, one-man show at Willard Gallery, New York (18 sculptures and 5 drawings from 1939–43). The Museum of Modern Art purchases its first Smith sculpture, *Head* (1938).

Summer 1944, moves back to Bolton Landing to work full-time on his artwork. Immediate post-war work is strongly symbolic in content; formal invention affected by Surrealist imagery and ideas. January 1946, one-man show at Willard and Buchholz Galleries (54 sculptures, 1936–45, including 30 made in 1944 and 1945).

1950–52
April, receives Guggenheim Foundation Fellowship (renewed 1951). Temporarily frees Smith from teaching and other jobs. The scale of his work expands dramatically, the forms become more lyrical and the content less narrative. Initiates practice of making sustained series of works over many years, beginning with the Agricola series (22 sculptures, 1951–57).

Summer 1950, exhibits in first European group show, the *International Open-Air Exhibition*, at Middelheim Park, Antwerp. December 1952, Smith and Dehner divorce. During the 1950s, is friendly with other Abstract Expressionist artists such as Jackson Pollock, Willem de Kooning, Franz Kline, and Michael Goldberg, as well as with younger artists, such as Kenneth Noland.

1953
Starts Tanktotem series (1953–60). Each Tanktotem incorporates parts of commercial boiler tops that Smith orders from a catalogue. Explores with increasing intensity abstract gestural imagery in drawing, using ink combined with egg yoke, a medium he invented.

January, signs of increased recognition as *Art News* lists Smith's 1952 sculpture exhibition at Willard and Kleeman Galleries one of the ten best shows of the year. April, while teaching at the University of Arkansas, marries Jean Freas of Washington, D.C. Six sculptures included in *Twelve Modern American Painters and Sculptors*, circulated by The Museum of Modern Art, New York to France, Switzerland, Germany, Sweden, Finland, and Norway.

1954–55
April, first child, Rebecca (Eve Athena Allen Katherine Rebecca) is born. June, work included in the *XXVII Venice Biennale*. Smith travels to Venice as a delegate to UNESCO's First International Congress of Plastic Arts; also visits France. Lectures on "Tradition," at Columbia University, New York.

Begins to place sculptures in the field around his home and studio at Bolton Landing. September to June 1955, teaches art at Indiana University, Bloomington, where he learns about forging from a local blacksmith. Begins Forging series and continues Tanktotems. Second child, Candida (Candida Kore Nicolina Rawley Helene), born in August.

1956–57
February, publishes "González: First Master of the Torch," in *Art News*, a tribute coinciding with González's retrospective at The Museum of Modern Art, New York. March, one-man show at Willard Gallery. No works are sold.

April through June, lives with his family in New York City. Paints steel surfaces in an expressionist style. October, begins Sentinels, nine tall vertical structures, several of which use industrial I-beams. 1957, begins to use new "reverse" stencil technique to make spray enamel works on paper and canvas. September, retrospective survey (sculptures, drawings, paintings, 1932–57) of his work opens at The Museum of Modern Art, New York.

1958–61
Smith and Freas separate and divorce. Work featured in one-man shows at the *XXIX Venice Biennale* (1958) and the *V Bienal of São Paulo* (1959). Eighteen of twenty-four sculptures completed in 1960 are painted, a dramatic increase from the past.

1961, begins Zig series (7 sculptures, 1961–64) and his most famous series, the Cubis (1961–65), 28 large-scale geometric stainless steel sculptures burnished to a highly reflective surface with a circular sander.

1962–63
May through July 1962, works in Voltri, Italy. Invited by Italian government to make two sculptures for exhibition in Spoleto during the *Fourth Festival of Two Worlds*, instead makes 27 sculptures in 30 days using a combination of tools, found objects, and created shapes. After his return to Bolton Landing, makes Voltri and Voltri-Bolton series (over 40, 1962–63) from old tools and machine parts shipped from Italy. Polychrome Circle (5 works, 1961) series characterized by reduced complexity and enlarged scale. Completes Primo Piano series, three large planar works in steel, painted white.

1964
Receives Brandeis University Creative Arts Award. Included in *Documenta III*, Kassel. Begins Wagons (3 sculptures, 1964) series. Large parts are cast at commercial foundry in Pennsylvania. Completes large series of enamel paintings of female nudes from photographs.

1965
February, appointed by President Lyndon B. Johnson to the National Council on the Arts. May 23, injured in an automobile crash near Bennington, Vermont. He dies that night.

Selected One-Person and Group Exhibitions

This list emphasizes exhibitions of drawings and major one-person sculpture shows; see the Biography for additional important group exhibitions. The artist's initials (DS) have been subtitled in exhibition titles containing his name; *denotes a group show

1938 East River Gallery, New York, *DS: Steel Sculpture*

1940 Neumann/Willard Gallery, New York, *DS*

1940 Willard Gallery, New York, *Medals for Dishonor by DS*

1941 The Museum of Modern Art, New York, *15 American Sculptors**

1943 Willard Gallery, New York, *DS*

1946 American Association of University Women and Marian Willard Gallery, New York, *DS*

1946 Buchholz Gallery (Curt Valentin) and Willard Gallery, New York, *The Sculpture of DS*

1947 Munson-Williams-Proctor Institute, Utica, New York, *DS*

1947 Willard Gallery, New York, *DS: Sculpture, 1946–1947*

1950 Willard Gallery, New York, *DS*

1951 Museu de Arte Moderna, São Paulo, *I Bienal de São Paulo*, U.S. Representation

1951 Willard Gallery, New York, *DS*

1952 Walker Art Center, Minneapolis, *Sculpture and Drawings: DS*

1952 Willard Gallery and Kleeman Galleries, New York, *DS: Sculpture and Drawing*

1953 Kootz Gallery, in association with the Willard Gallery, New York, *DS: New Sculpture*

1953 Willard Gallery, New York, *DS: Drawings*

1954 Contemporary Arts Center in the Cincinnati Art Museum, *DS: Sculpture, Drawings, Graphics*

1954 Willard Gallery, New York, *DS*

1954 *XXVII Venice Biennale* (American Representation), *2 Pittori, 3 Scultori [2 Painters, 3 Sculptors]**

1956 Willard Gallery, New York, *DS: Sculpture—Drawings, 1954–56*

1957 Fine Arts Associates (Otto M. Gerson), New York, *Sculpture by DS*

1957 The Museum of Modern Art, New York, *DS*

1958 World's Fair, United States Pavilion, Brussels*

1958 *XXIX Biennale di Venezia*, U.S. Representation, *Lipton, Rothko, Smith and Tobey**

1959 French & Company, New York, *DS: Paintings and Drawings*

1959 Kassel, Germany, *Dokumenta II: Skulptur**

1959 Museu de Arte Moderna, São Paulo, *V Bienal de São Paulo*, U.S. Representation*

1960 Everett Ellin Gallery, Los Angeles, *DS: Sculpture & Drawings*

1960 French & Company, New York, *Sculpture by DS*

1961 Otto Gerson Gallery, New York, *DS: Recent Sculpture*

1964 Institute of Contemporary Art, University of Pennsylvania, Philadelphia, *DS Sculpture and Drawings*

1964 Kassel, Germany, *Documenta III**

1964 Marlborough-Gerson Gallery, New York, *DS*

1965 Los Angeles County Museum of Art, *DS: A Memorial Exhibition*

1966 Fogg Art Museum, Harvard University, Cambridge, Massachusetts, *DS: 1906–1965*

1966 Rijksmuseum Kröller-Müller, Otterlo (international travelling exhibition, organized by the International Council of The Museum of Modern Art, New York), *DS 1906–1965*

1968 The Museum of Modern Art, New York, *Dada, Surrealism and Their Heritage**

1969 Solomon R. Guggenheim Museum, New York, *DS*

1973 Knoedler Contemporary Art, New York, *DS: Drawings*

1973 The Hyde Collection, Glens Falls, New York, *DS of Bolton Landing: Sculpture and Drawings*

1974 Knoedler Contemporary Art, New York, *DS (1912–1965)*

1974 The Museum of Fine Arts, Houston, *The Great Decade of American Abstraction: Modernist Art 1960 to 1970**

1976 Staatsgalerie Stuttgart, Graphische Sammlung, Stuttgart, *DS: Zeichnungen* [*DS: Drawings*]

1976 Storm King Art Center, Mountainville, New York, *DS*

1977 M. Knoedler & Co., New York, *DS*

1978 M. Knoedler & Co., New York, *DS (1906–1965)*

1978 National Gallery of Art, Washington, D.C., *American Art at Mid-Century: The Subjects of the Artist**

1979 Hans Strelow Gallery, Düsseldorf, *DS: Important Drawings from the Estate of the American Sculptor (1906–1965)*

1979 Whitney Museum of American Art, New York, *DS: The Drawings*

1980 M. Knoedler & Co., New York, *DS: Drawings with Color*

1980 Serpentine Gallery, London, *DS: Sculpture and Drawings*

1981 Edmonton Art Gallery, Alberta, Canada, *DS: The Formative Years: Sculptures and Drawings from the 1930s and 1940s*

1981 M. Knoedler & Co., New York, *DS: Spray Paintings and Works on Paper*

1981 Mekler Gallery, Los Angeles, *DS: Drawings for Sculpture: 1954–1964*

1982 Hirshhorn Museum and Sculpture Garden, Washington, D.C., *DS: Painter, Sculptor, Draftsman*

1982 National Gallery of Art, Washington, D.C., *DS*

1983 Arts Club of Chicago, *DS: Spray Paintings, Drawings, Sculpture*

1983 M. Knoedler & Co., New York, *DS: Sculpture, Painting, Drawing*

1983 Washburn Gallery, New York, *DS: Paintings from 1930–1947*

1984 M. Knoedler & Co., New York, *DS: Sculpture, Painting and Drawing of the Fifties*

1984 Whitney Museum of American Art, New York, *The Third Dimension: Sculpture of the New York School**

1985 Anthony d'Offay Gallery, London, *DS: Sprays from Bolton Landing*

1985 International Exhibitions Foundation, Washington, D.C., *The Drawings of DS* (travelled nationally)

1986 Centre Georges Pompidou, Paris, *Qu'est-ce que c'est la sculpture moderne?*

1986 Galerie Hans Strelow, Düsseldorf, *DS, Die reifen Jahre 1951–1965 Skulpturen und Zeichnungen [DS, The Mature Years 1951–1965: Sculpture and Drawings]*

1986 Kunstsammlung Nordrhein-Westfalen, Düsseldorf, *DS, Skulpturen, Zeichnungen* [*DS, Sculpture and Drawings*]

1986 M. Knoedler & Co., New York, *DS: Drawings and Sculpture*

1987 Dallas Museum of Art, *A Century of Modern Sculpture: The Patsy and Raymond Nasher Collection*

1987 Washburn Gallery, New York, *DS: Paintings from the 1930's*

1988 Anthony d'Offay Gallery, London, *DS: Drawings of the Fifties*

1990 Heide Park and Art Gallery, Bulleen, Victoria, Australia, *DS: Drawings and Sculpture*

1990 Knoedler & Company, New York, *DS. Nudes*

1990 Margo Leavin Gallery, Los Angeles, *DS: Works on Paper*

1990 Montclair Art Museum, New Jersey, *DS, Nudes: Drawings and Paintings from 1927–1964*

1990 Washburn Gallery, New York, *DS: Paintings into Sculpture*

1991 The Henry Moore Centre for the Study of Sculpture, Leeds City Art Galleries, London, *DS, Medals for Dishonor 1937–1940*

1992 Knoedler & Company, New York, *DS: Sculpture and Drawings*

1993 Solomon R. Guggenheim Museum, New York, *Picasso and the Age of Iron**

1994 Margo Leavin Gallery, Los Angeles, *DS, The Charcoal Drawings: 1958*

1994 Matthew Marks Gallery, *New York, DS, Medals for Dishonor, 1937–1940* (national tour organized by Independent Curators Incorporated, New York)

1994 Sezon, Shizuoka, Shiga, Kawamura, Japan, *DS*

1995 Knoedler Company, New York, *DS: To and From the Figure*

1995 Prada MilanoArte, Milan, *David Smith in Italy*

1995 Washburn Gallery, New York, *DS: The Inspiration of Music*

1996 IVAM (Instituto Valenciano de Arte Moderno), Centro Julio González, Spain, *DS*

1996 Knoedler & Company, New York and Italy, *DS and Italy: Voltri Landscapes and Sprays*

1997 Storm King Art Center, Mountainville, New York, *The Fields of DS* (3 year-long exhibitions, 1997–1999)

1998 Gagosian Gallery, New York, *Painted Steel: The Late Works of DS*

1999 Tel Aviv Museum of Art, *DS: Paintings, Sculptures and Medals*

2000 Douglas F. Cooley Memorial Art Gallery, Reed College, Portland, Oregon, *DS: Two into Three Dimensions* (organized by Arts Management Services/American Federation of Arts, New York, travelled nationally)

2000 Gagosian Gallery, New York, *DS: The Last Nudes*

2000 Indianapolis Museum of Art, *Crossroads of American sculpture: George Rickey, John Chamberlain, Robert Indiana, William T. Wiley, Bruce Nauman**

2001 Margo Leavin Gallery, Los Angeles, *DS Ink Drawings from 1957*

2003 École national supérieure des beaux-arts, Chapelle des Petits-Augustins, Paris, *Dessins de DS: un choix d'Alain Kirili* [*Drawings by DS: Selected by Alain Kirili*]

2003 Fogg Art Museum, Harvard University, Cambridge, Massachusetts, *Lois Orswell, DS and Modern Art*

2004 Gagosian Gallery, New York, *DS, Related Clues: Drawings, Paintings and Sculpture 1931–1964*

2004 IVAM (Instituto Valenciano de Arte Moderno), Centro Julio González, Spain, *DS: Dibujante. Entre Eros y Tánatos* [*DS: Draftsman. Between Eros and Thanatos*]